The Principles of
Heterocyclic Chemistry

The Principles of Heterocyclic Chemistry

ALAN R. KATRITZKY

M.A., D.PHIL., PH.D., SC.D.
*Dean of the School of Chemical Sciences,
University of East Anglia, Norwich, England*

and

J. M. LAGOWSKI

B.S., M.S., PH.D.
*Research Scientist, Genetics Foundation,
The University of Texas, Austin, Texas, U.S.A.*

1968

ACADEMIC PRESS   New York and London

Preface

We published in 1960 a textbook entitled *Heterocyclic Chemistry*. This was aimed at rationalizing the subject in terms of the electronic theory of organic chemistry, which has been so helpful in promoting the understanding of aliphatic and benzenoid chemistry.

This work received an enthusiastic reception as far as overall conception and accuracy were concerned. However, it was generally considered to contain more material than required by the student, and to be somewhat difficult to read because of the terse style. In this revision, the text has been largely rewritten. The essential organization has been retained, but the amount of factual matter reduced and the explanatory passages simplified in an endeavour to make the book easily digestible. A limited quantity of important new work has been incorporated. We feel that the book contains the essential heterocyclic chemistry required by an Undergraduate or Graduate student for his course-work, and it is hoped that it will be found stimulating by many a more senior teacher and researcher.

A. R. KATRITZKY
J. M. LAGOWSKI

Norwich and Austin
August, 1965

v

Contents

CHAPTER ONE

Introduction

Heterocyclic chemistry is of the greatest theoretical and practical importance. The large quantity of factual matter can make it appear to be very complex, and sometimes the method by which it is taught serves only to emphasize this to the student: a few ring systems are selected, a list of the preparations and the properties of each is given, and then attention is turned to natural products. It is the aim of this book to present a unified account of fundamental heterocyclic chemistry with the emphasis placed on the correlations between the methods of preparation and the properties of the various ring systems. Further, it is hoped to show that an encyclopaedic memory is not a prerequisite for the acquisition of a working knowledge of the subject; heterocyclic chemistry is as logical as aliphatic or benzenoid chemistry, and understanding the facts is more important – and easier – than learning them. To understand heterocyclic chemistry a reasonable knowledge of aliphatic and benzenoid chemistry is essential; possession of this is assumed. Frequent reference is made to electronic theory in this book, and because of its importance a brief summary is presented in Section **1.2**.

1. Use of this Book by the Undergraduate Student

This should begin with a careful reading of the Introduction. The key chapters are 2 and 4 which deal with six- and five-membered rings, respectively, containing one annular nitrogen, oxygen, or sulphur atom. The material has been arranged with the object of a logical presentation and not with regard to the relative importance of the facts. Attention is therefore drawn to summaries of several sections of these chapters: in Chapter 2, ring syntheses are summarized in Section **2.II**, reactions of the aromatic nuclei in Section **2.III**, reactions of substituents in Section **2.IV**, and preparations of substituted compounds in Section **2.IV.C**. The corresponding summaries in Chapter 4 appear in Sections **4.II**, **4.III**, and **4.IV**, respectively.

1

2. Fundamental Concepts of the Electronic Theory of Organic Chemistry*

Organic chemistry has now developed to the point where the vast majority of reactions can be explained and correlated as a succession of individual steps which in turn can be classified into a few simple, basic reaction types. In every organic reaction bonds are broken and/or formed. A chemical bond consists of two electrons shared by two atoms, and it can be formed (or broken) in three ways.

(*i*) One of the atoms contributes both electrons to the bond either from a lone pair

$$A \overset{\frown}{:} B \longrightarrow A^+ : B^-$$

or from another bond, often a multiple bond

$$D \overset{\frown}{=\!\!=\!\!A} B \longrightarrow D^+\!\!-\!\!A\!\!-\!\!B^-$$

(the curved arrow represents the movement of an electron pair), and the atoms become formally charged. Reactions of this type, called generalized ionic reactions, are by far the most important. The atom, molecule, or ion which contributes the electron pair is called a nucleophilic reagent and that which accepts it an electrophilic reagent.

(*ii*) Each atom contributes one electron to the bond

$$A \overset{\frown}{\cdot\cdot} B \longrightarrow A : B$$

(the dotted arrows represent the movement of single electrons). Reactions of this type are known as free radical reactions because at least one of the reactants or products must be a free radical, i.e. contain an unpaired electron.

(*iii*) The bond is formed or broken in a cyclic transition state (1 $\longrightarrow$ 2). It might at first appear that the electrons can move either in pairs as in (3) or (4) or as single electrons (5), but modern theory shows that it is meaningless to try to distinguish between these possibilities and indicates that the cyclic transition state should be treated as a distinct reaction type.

| 1 | 2 | 3 | 4 | 5 |

3. Relationship of Heterocyclic and Carbocyclic Aromatic Compounds

Carbocyclic compounds can be divided into aromatic and alicyclic

---

* For a comprehensive treatment, see (*inter alia*) the following textbooks. Cram and Hammond, *Organic Chemistry*, 2nd Ed., McGraw-Hill, New York, 1964. Roberts and Caserio, *Basic Principles of Organic Chemistry*, Benjamin, 1964.

types. The chemistry of the alicyclic compounds is in general similar to that of their aliphatic analogues, but that of aromatic compounds involves additional principles. Heterocyclic compounds can be divided similarly. Again, new principles are involved mainly in the chemistry of the heteroaromatic compounds, and it is on them that the emphasis in this book is placed.

Aromatic compounds possess five-, six-, or seven-membered rings* in which each of the ring atoms is in the same plane and has a *p*-orbital perpendicular to this plane (i.e. takes part in the unsaturation) and in which six π-electrons (the aromatic sextet) are associated with each ring.

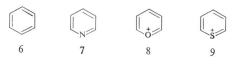

$$6 \qquad 7 \qquad 8 \qquad 9$$

Six-membered aromatic heterocycles are derived from benzene (6) by replacing CH groups with N, O^+, or S^+ which are isoelectronic with the CH group.† One CH group can be replaced to give pyridine (7), the pyrylium ion (8), and the thiapyrylium ion (9). Replacement of two or more CH groups with retention of aromaticity is possible.

The five-membered aromatic heterocycles thiophene (10), pyrrole (11), and furan (12) are formally derived from benzene by replacement of two CH groups with one S, NH, or O, each of which can contribute *two* electrons to the aromatic sextet.† Other five-membered aromatic heterocycles are derived from compounds (10), (11), and (12) by further replacement of CH groups with N, O^+, or S^+.

$$10 \qquad 11 \qquad 12$$

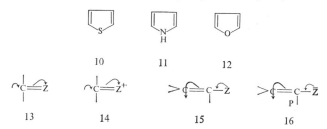

$$13 \qquad 14 \qquad 15 \qquad 16$$

The basic principles governing the degree and type of reactivity

---

* Recently carbocyclic aromatic rings of large size have been recognized, but little is known about their hetero derivatives. For reasons of space and since no overall treatment is yet possible, heterocycles with seven- and larger-membered rings are not considered in this book.

† A few aromatic compounds with other heteroatoms are known, e.g. heterocycles containing arsenic, boron, phosphorus, selenium, silicon, and tellurium.

shown by heteroaromatic compounds are familiar from aliphatic and benzenoid chemistry. Three are very important.

(*i*) Oxygen, nitrogen, or sulphur multiply-bonded to carbon can accept the whole of a shared pair of π-electrons (13) and thus allow a nucleophilic reagent to attack the carbon atom, as in many common reactions of carbonyl compounds. The attack by a nucleophilic reagent is easier when the heteroatom carries a positive charge (14).

(*ii*) A shared pair of electrons on oxygen, nitrogen, or sulphur adjacent to an unsaturated system can be made available for reaction through that system (15). This can also happen when the heteroatom carries a negative charge (16); the alkylation of the acetoacetate anion on carbon is an analogous reaction in aliphatic chemistry.

(*iii*) Aromatic compounds tend to 'revert to type', i.e. to return to their initial system of unsaturation, if it is disturbed. Thus, the reaction of bromine with both benzene (17–19) and ethylene (20–22) is very similar in the first step but different in the second step in that reversion to type takes place in the aromatic series only.

These basic principles give much insight into the reactions of aromatic heterocyclic compounds. For six-membered heteroaromatic compounds, principles (*i*) and (*iii*) apply: for five-membered rings with one heteroatom, principles (*ii*) and (*iii*) apply. For five-membered heteroaromatic rings with two or more heteroatoms, principles (*i*), (*ii*), and (*iii*) are all applicable.

4. Arrangement of the Book

Chapters 2 and 3 are concerned with the chemistry of the six-membered ring compounds containing one or more heteroatoms. Chapters 4 and 5 deal with the corresponding five-membered ring compounds. A familiarity with Chapter 2 is essential for understanding Chapter 3, and Chapter 5 assumes a knowledge of the material presented in Chapters 2, 3, and 4. Three- and four-membered rings are discussed in Chapter 6. Physical properties of representative heterocyclic compounds are collected and discussed in Chapter 7.

The arrangement of Chapters 2–5 is the same in each case. An introductory section surveys the various ring types, gives the systems of nomenclature and numbering, and mentions a few important natural and synthetic compounds. Syntheses starting from aliphatic and carbocyclic compounds are then given. The preparation of one heterocyclic compound from another is considered as a reaction of the starting material. The reactions of aromatic and non-aromatic compounds are discussed separately in each chapter. For convenience, the reactions of aromatic compounds are divided into the reactions of the ring and the reactions of the substituent; this division is at times rather artificial, but it has many advantages. In general, a reaction in which a substituent is altered is considered as a reaction of the substituent. Fused benzene rings are treated as substituents; for example, quinoline is considered as a substituted pyridine.

The mechanisms of the reactions by which heterocyclic rings are prepared from acyclic or carbocyclic compounds are not discussed in detail because such a discussion appears to belong to aliphatic and carbocyclic chemistry rather than to heterocyclic chemistry. Moreover, the general features are usually obvious by inspection. Carbon-to-carbon bonds are frequently formed by aldol- and Claisen-type reactions or by attack of an electrophilic reagent (e.g. a carbonyl or carboxyl group, a halide or a diazonium ion) on a benzene ring or double bond. Bonds from carbon to oxygen, nitrogen, or sulphur atoms are usually formed by nucleophilic displacements, carbonyl addition reactions, or Michael additions. Elimination reactions are also frequently encountered.

5. Conventions

Arabic numerals are always used to denote the positions of substituents in actual compounds; Greek letters are used to indicate the relative positions of the substituent and the heteroatom. For example, 2-picoline, 1-methylisoquinoline, and 6-methylphenanthridine are all considered to have an α-methyl group, because in each case the methyl is on the carbon adjacent to the nitrogen atom.

23   24   25   26   27   28

Diagrams of monocyclic compounds are oriented so that the numbering starts at the bottom and proceeds counter-clockwise around the ring (cf. formulae 39–49). Diagrams of polycyclic compounds in which one ring is heterocyclic are consistently oriented with the heterocyclic ring in the same position as that used for the corresponding monocyclic compounds. This emphasizes their similarity. In a few cases this is different from current practice (or practices); e.g. in this book isoquinoline is shown as (23) rather than as (24) and pyrimidine as (25) rather than as one of structures (26)–(28). Diagrams of polycyclic compounds containing two or more heterocyclic rings are usually oriented in the conventional manner. Double bonds are always indicated, but hydrogen atoms attached to cyclic carbon atoms are not usually shown.

The letter Z is used to indicate an O or S atom, an NH, NMe, NPh group, etc. Alkyl and aryl groups are denoted by R and Ar, respectively; Y indicates an unspecified substituent. Methyl, ethyl, propyl, acetyl, *p*-toluenesulphonyl, and phenyl groups and halogen atoms are represented by Me, Et, Pr, Ac, Ts, Ph, and X, respectively. E^+ and Nu^- represent electrophilic and nucleophilic reagents.

An effort has been made to give an idea of the conditions under which reactions are effected. To do this with a minimal expenditure of space, approximate temperatures and the formulae of reagents and solvents are given in parentheses in the cursive text or above the arrows in the diagrams.

In some diagrams arrows have been used to indicate the place or alternative places at which reaction occurs. These arrows are short and thick (➔) to avoid confusion with the curved arrows (⌒) used to represent the movement of an electron pair.

6. Nomenclature

An attempt has been made to follow the system of nomenclature used in *Chemical Abstracts* and approved by the International Union of Pure and Applied Chemistry.* The few exceptions are indicated. Some of the rules of systematic nomenclature are collected here, and examples of their use are given at the end of this section. Important trivial names are listed at the beginning of individual chapters.

The types of heteroatoms present in a ring are indicated by prefixes: 'oxa', 'thia', and 'aza' denote oxygen, sulphur, and nitrogen,

---

* For a detailed discussion, see *Chemical Abstracts*, Introduction to 1962 Subject Index to Volume 56 and subsequent annual revisions; *Handbook for Chemical Society Authors*, Chemical Society, London, 1961.

respectively (the final 'a' is elided before a vowel). Two or more identical heteroatoms are indicated by 'dioxa', 'triaza', etc., and different heteroatoms by combining the above prefixes in order of preference, i.e. O, S, and N.

Ring size and the number of double bonds are indicated by the suffixes shown in the table.* Maximum unsaturation is defined as the largest possible number of non-cumulative double bonds (O, S, and N having valencies of 2, 2, and 3, respectively). Partially saturated rings are indicated by the prefixes 'dihydro', 'tetrahydro', etc.

Ring size	Rings with nitrogen			Rings without nitrogen		
	Max. unsat.	One double bond	Satd.	Max. unsat.	One double bond	Satd.
3	-irine	–	-iridine	-irene	–	-irane
4	-ete	-etine	-etidine	-ete	-etene	-etane
5	-ole	-oline	-olidine	-ole	-olene	-olane
6	-ine	–	–	-in	–	-ane
7	-epine	–	–	-epin	–	-epane

Numbering starts at an oxygen, sulphur, or nitrogen atom (in decreasing order of preference) and continues in such a way that the heteroatoms are assigned the lowest possible numbers. Other things being equal, numbering starts at a substituted rather than at a multiply-bonded nitrogen atom. In compounds with maximum unsaturation, if the double bonds can be arranged in more than one way, their positions are defined by indicating the nitrogen or carbon atoms which are not multiply bonded, and consequently carry an 'extra' hydrogen atom, by '$1H$-', '$2H$-', etc. In partially saturated compounds, the positions of the hydrogen atoms can be indicated by '1,2-dihydro', etc. (together with the $1H$-type notation if necessary); alternatively, the positions of the double bonds can be specified, e.g. 'Δ^3-' indicates that a double bond is between atoms 3 and 4.

A positively charged annular nitrogen atom is denoted by adding the suffix 'onium'. There is no general rule for designating positively charged cyclic oxygen and sulphur atoms.

The nomenclature used for compounds containing ring carbonyl groups is in a confused state. The presence of a ring carbonyl group is indicated by the suffix '-one' and its position by a numeral, e.g. '1-one', '2-one', etc.;† the numeral indicating the position of the

---

* Suffixes for 8-, 9-, and 10-membered rings also exist but have been little used.

† The prefix 'keto' should be used with discretion; carbonyl groups adjacent to heteroatoms are not ketonic.

carbonyl group is placed, according to present *Chemical Abstracts* convention, immediately before the name of the parent compound when numerals are not used to designate the position of hetero-atoms, if numerals are so used they are placed immediately before the suffix. Compounds containing groups (30) or (33) are frequently named either as derivatives of (29) and (32) or of (31) and (34); both systems have their advantages and disadvantages. According to

29   30   31   32   33   34

Chemical Abstracts, 'A cyclic ketone often must be regarded as formed by substitution, not of the parent compound itself, but of a hydro derivative of it, but it is convenient to form names for such functional derivatives from the parent compound.' In practice, however, *Chemical Abstracts* does not appear to treat compounds containing carbonyl groups consistently: e.g. (35) is named 2-pyrazolin-5-one, which is derived from the dihydro form of the parent, 2-pyrazoline (36), whereas the name for (37), 2(1*H*)-pyra-

35   36   37   38

zinone, is derived from the aromatic compound pyrazine (38). An attempt has been made in this book to follow *Chemical Abstracts'* usage; unfortunately this does not appear to be adequately defined, but it apparently means that names for five-membered rings are based on structures (31) and (34) while those for six-membered rings are based on (29) and (32). The position of the extra hydrogen atom is indicated by the '1*H*-' notation if this is necessary for clarity.

Ring C=S and C=NH groups are denoted by the suffixes 'thione' and 'onimine';* cf. 'one' for the C=O group.

39   40   41

oxaziridine   2-methyl-4*H*-oxete   1,3-dioxole

* Compounds containing this group are named as dihydro-imino derivatives of the parent ring system by *Chemical Abstracts*.

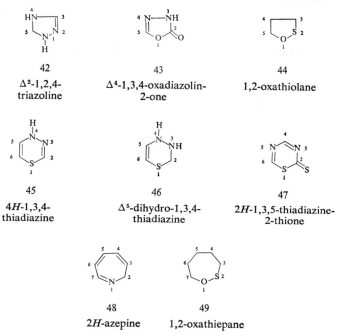

42

Δ²-1,2,4-triazoline

43

Δ⁴-1,3,4-oxadiazolin-2-one

44

1,2-oxathiolane

45

4*H*-1,3,4-thiadiazine

46

Δ⁵-dihydro-1,3,4-thiadiazine

47

2*H*-1,3,5-thiadiazine-2-thione

48

2*H*-azepine

49

1,2-oxathiepane

Examples of the application of these systematic rules of nomen-clature are shown in formulae (39) to (49). In general, complicated examples have been selected because the simpler ring systems usually possess trivial names, which are given in the individual chapters.

7. The Literature of Heterocyclic Chemistry

Space considerations preclude giving references to original papers in this book, however some important secondary sources which are concerned primarily with heterocyclic chemistry are mentioned here.

(*a*) *Advances in Heterocyclic Chemistry*, edited by Katritzky (pub-lished by Academic Press), is a series aimed at making available up-to-date reviews of a wide variety of topics in this field. Since the series commenced in 1963, eight volumes containing some 50 reviews have appeared. Further publication of one or two volumes per year is planned.

(*b*) *Physical Methods in Heterocyclic Chemistry*, edited by Katritzky (published by Academic Press), appeared in 1963 in two parts. The application of physical methods to heterocyclic compounds is discussed and forms ideal background reading for Chapter 7 of this book.

(*c*) Heterocyclic chemistry is surveyed in the series *Heterocyclic Compounds*, edited by Elderfield (published by John Wiley & Sons Inc.). Seven volumes have appeared: I, monocyclic compounds containing one heteroatom (1950); II, polycyclic compounds containing one annular oxygen atom (1951); III, benzopyrroles (1952); IV, benzopyridines (1952); V, compounds containing two heteroatoms in a five-membered ring (1957); VI, compounds containing two heteroatoms in a six-membered ring (1957); VII, polycyclic compounds with two heteroatoms in different rings, five- and six-membered heterocycles containing three heteroatoms (1961). One further volume is stated to be in preparation.

(*d*) *The Chemistry of Heterocyclic Compounds*, edited by Weissberger [published by Interscience (Wiley)], is to treat the subject in 28 volumes, but is as yet incomplete. Twenty volumes (some published in several parts) have appeared (December 1966) (date of publication and author given in parentheses): the heterocyclic derivatives of P, As, Sb, Bi, and Si (1950, Mann); six-membered heterocyclic nitrogen compounds with four condensed rings (1951, Allen); thiophenes (1952, Hartough); five-membered heterocyclic compounds with N and S, or N, S, and O (except thiazole) (1952, Bambas); condensed pyridazine and pyrazine rings (1953, Simpson); imidazoles, part I (1953, Hofmann); condensed thiophenes (1954, Hartough and Meisel); indoles and carbazoles (1954, Sumpter and Miller); acridines (1956, Acheson); 1,2,3- and 1,2,4-triazines, tetrazines, and pentazines (1957, Erickson, Wiley, and Wystrach); phenazines (1957, Swan and Felton); six-membered heterocyclic nitrogen compounds with three condensed rings (1958, Allen); *s*-triazines (1959, Rapoport and Smolin); pyridine and its derivatives (pt. I, 1960; pt. II, 1961; pt. III, 1962; pt. IV, 1964; Klingsberg); hetercyclic compounds with bridgehead nitrogen atoms (pts. 1 and 2, 1961, Mosby); pyrimidines (1962, Brown); five- and six-membered compounds with nitrogen and oxygen (excluding oxazoles) (1962, Wiley); cyanine dyes and related compounds (1963, Hamer); three- and four-membered rings (pts. 1 and 2, 1964, Weissberger); pyrazolones, pyrazolidones, and derivatives (1964, Wiley and Wiley).

(*e*) In *The Chemistry of the Carbon Compounds*, edited by Rodd (published by Elsevier), Volume 4, which has appeared in three parts, is devoted to a comprehensive survey of heterocyclic chemistry.

(*f*) In addition to the above series, which will give reasonably complete coverage, numerous topics have been treated in monographs and review articles. A chapter in Volume 6 of *Advances in Heterocyclic Chemistry* [see (*a*) above] lists these secondary sources by subject.

CHAPTER TWO

Six-Membered Rings with One Heteroatom

I. NOMENCLATURE AND IMPORTANT COMPOUNDS

1. Monocyclic Nitrogen-Containing Compounds

(*a*) *Nomenclature.* The systematic nomenclature is shown in formulae (1)–(7); nuclear positions are indicated by arabic numerals, or, less frequently, by Greek letters (cf. 1).

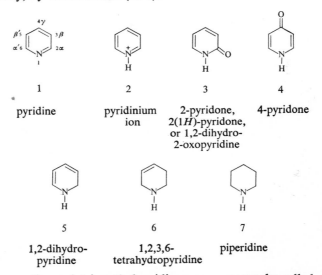

1	2	3	4
pyridine	pyridinium ion	2-pyridone, 2(1*H*)-pyridone, or 1,2-dihydro-2-oxopyridine	4-pyridone

5	6	7
1,2-dihydro-pyridine	1,2,3,6-tetrahydropyridine	piperidine

Mono-, di-, and tri-methylpyridines are commonly called picolines, lutidines, and collidines, respectively; the specific isomer is denoted, e.g. 2,6-lutidine. Picolinic, nicotinic, and isonicotinic acids are the trivial names for the 2-, 3-, and 4-pyridinecarboxylic acids, respectively.

(*b*) *Occurrence.* Coal tar and bone oil contain pyridine, picolines,

12

lutidines, and collidines. Nicotinamide (8) and pyridoxine (9) are examples of pyridine derivatives with important metabolic roles, while nicotine (10) exemplifies the pyridine–pyrrolidine class of alkaloids.

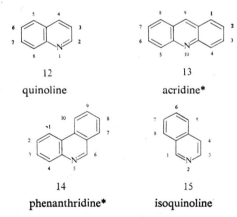

8	9	10	11
nicotinamide (B-complex vitamin)	pyridoxine (vitamin B₆)	nicotine (tobacco)	isoniazid (tuberculostat)

(*c*) *Uses.* Pyridine is used extensively as a solvent and as a synthetic intermediate. Some pyridine and piperidine derivatives are used pharmaceutically, e.g. isoniazid (11).

2. Benzopyridines

The benzopyridines and their systems of numbering are shown in structures (12)–(15). Important trivial names include quinaldine and lepidine for 2- and 4-methylquinoline, respectively, and carbostyril for 2-quinolone.

12

quinoline

13

acridine*

14

phenanthridine*

15

isoquinoline

* The following systems of numbering for acridine and phenanthridine are also frequently encountered in the literature.

The parent compounds and some lower homologues occur in coal tar. Many important alkaloids contain benzopyridine nuclei; e.g. quinoline and isoquinoline ring systems occur in quinine (16, Y = OMe) and papaverine (17), respectively. Acriflavine (18) and mepacrin (19) are dibenzopyridine derivatives used as chemotherapeutic agents.

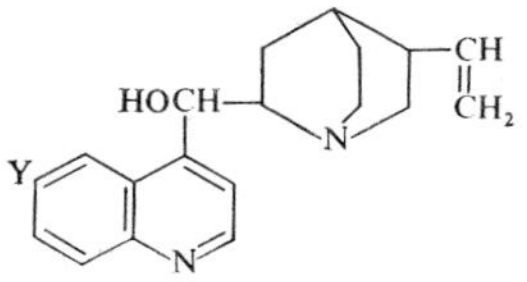

16

Y = H, cinchonine
Y = OMe, quinine

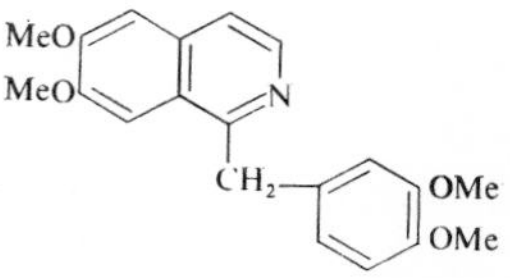

17

papaverine

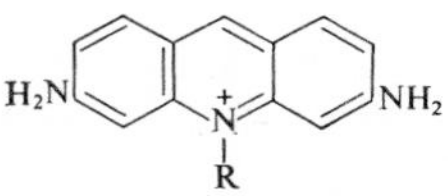

18

acriflavine
(antiseptic, a
mixture of R = H
and Me)

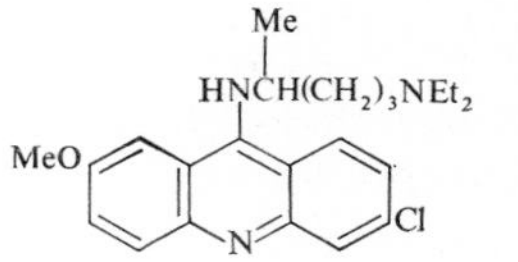

19

mepacrin, atebrin,
or quinacrin
(antimalarial)

3. Monocyclic Oxygen- and Sulphur-Containing Compounds

(*a*) *Nomenclature.* The 'aromatic' oxygen-containing nuclei comprise the pyrylium ion and 2- and 4-pyrones (20–22); the corresponding sulphur-containing nuclei are the thiopyrylium ion and 2- and 4-thiopyrones. Valency requirements do not permit the existence of an uncharged oxygen analogue of pyridine itself, although sulphur analogues of this type have recently been prepared (e.g. 23).

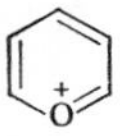

20

pyrylium
cation

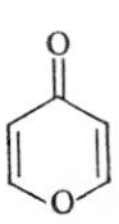

21

4-pyrone,
γ-pyrone, or
4-pyranone

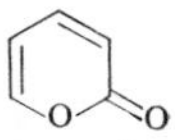

22

2-pyrone
or
α-pyrone

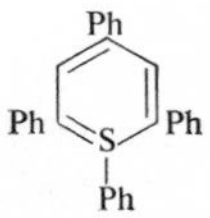

23

The uncharged parent ring systems with two double bonds are called pyran or thiopyran; the position of the 'extra' hydrogen atom must be indicated to distinguish between the two isomers (cf. 24 and 25). Two dihydro-pyrans (26, 27) and -thiopyrans are possible; the *delta* notation is used to indicate the position of the remaining double bond. The fully reduced derivatives are called tetrahydro-pyran and -thiopyran.

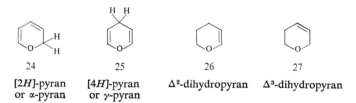

24	25	26	27
[2*H*]-pyran or α-pyran	[4*H*]-pyran or γ-pyran	Δ²-dihydropyran	Δ³-dihydropyran

(*b*) *Occurrence*. Pyrones occur as natural products, e.g. kojic acid (28). Sugars containing a six-membered tetrahydropyran ring (29) are called pyranoses.

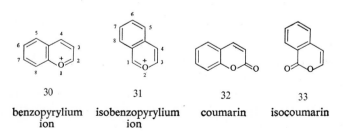

28	29
kojic acid	pyranose sugar

4. Monobenzo-Pyrones and -Pyrylium Salts

(*a*) *Nomenclature*. Important monobenzo derivatives, their trivial names, and the systems of numbering for the 2,3- and 3,4-benzo series are shown in structures (30)–(36). An additional system of nomenclature is in use for the 2- and 3-phenyl derivatives (37)–(41), an important class of plant pigments.

30	31	32	33
benzopyrylium ion	isobenzopyrylium ion	coumarin	isocoumarin

34	35	36	37
chromone	4*H*-chromene	chroman	flavylium ion

38	39	40	41
flavone	flavanone	flavan	isoflavone

(*b*) *Occurrence.* Simple derivatives of these bicyclic systems occur in nature, e.g. vitamin E (42).

Natural products derived from the phenylated nuclei (37–41) occur widely. The anthocyanidins, polyhydroxyflavylium salts (cf. 37), are the aglycones of the naturally occurring glycosidic pigments, the anthocyanins, which impart bright blue or red colours to flowers and fruits. The yellow or brown pigments of wood, cell sap, etc. are polyhydroxy derivatives of (38)–(41) in which some of the hydroxyl groups may be methylated or attached to a sugar residue. In the following summary of the positions at which oxygen functions occur, a marked similarity can be discerned, reflecting common biogenetic pathways.

POSITIONS OF HYDROXYL, METHOXYL, OR GLYCOSYL
GROUPS IN NATURALLY OCCURRING PIGMENTS

Type of Pigment	Usual	Frequent	Rare
Anthocyanin	3, 5, 7, 4′	3′, 5′	–
Flavone	3, 5, 7, 4′	6, 8, 3′	2′, 5′
Isoflavone	5, 7, 4′	–	6, 2′, 3′
Flavanone	5, 7, 4′	3, 3′	6, 8, 2′, 5′
Flavan	3, 5, 7, 4′	2, 4, 3′	5′

5. Dibenzo-Pyrones and -Pyrylium Salts

The parent compounds, their names, and system of numbering are shown in structures (44)–(46).

The dye fluorescein (43) is a xanthene derivative. Eosin, the sodium salt of 2,4,5,7-tetrabromofluorescein, is used as an absorption indicator for the argentometric titration of halides, etc.

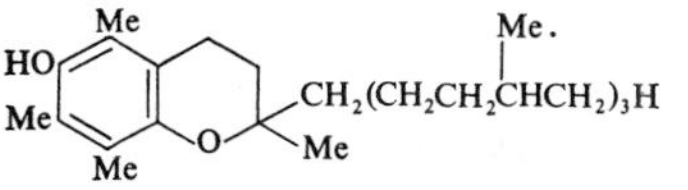

42

vitamin E

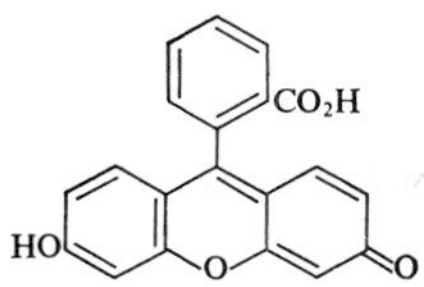

43

fluorescein

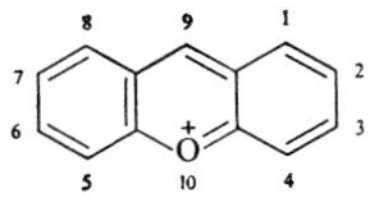

44

xanthylium ion

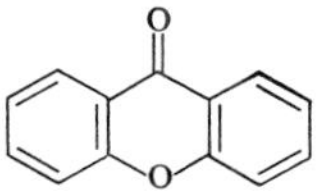

45

xanthone*

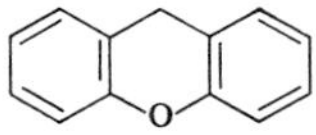

46

xanthene

II. RING SYNTHESES

A. GENERAL SURVEY

In general, syntheses in which a C–Z bond is formed in the last stage are more important for the preparation of monocyclic compounds, whereas those syntheses in which a C–C bond is formed in the last stage are important for the benzo derivatives. Where ring closure takes place by formation of a C–Z bond, the starting material or reaction intermediate must contain a five-carbon atom chain. The degree of unsaturation of the heterocyclic product depends on the nature of this chain: Pent-2-ene-1,5-diones or pentane-1,3,5-triones give aromatic products (47 → 48; 49 → 50); pentane-1,5 diones yield dihydro compounds (51 → 52) (which are sometimes oxidized *in situ*); and other 1,5-disubstituted pentane derivatives and certain cyclopentanes form tetra- or hexa-hydro products (53, 55 → 54).

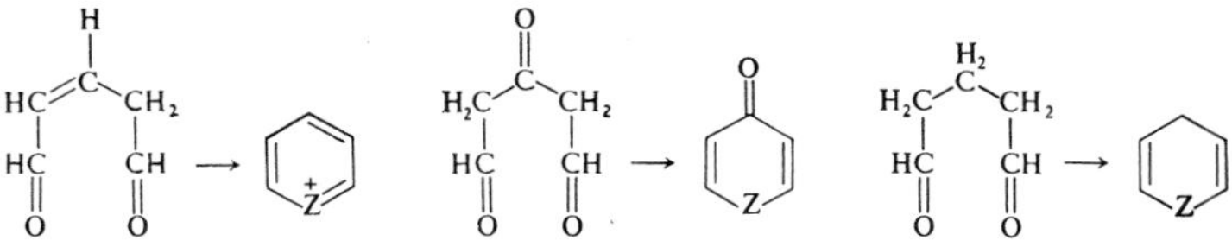

47   48   49   50   51   52

Of the syntheses involving C–C bond formation, those in which the C3–C4 bond is formed (56 → 57) are more important than those involving C2–C3 bond formation (58 → 57). Among the methods

---

* The *Chemical Abstracts* preferred name is 9-xanthenone.

of this type, several important ring closures proceed by reaction of
a carbonyl group with an aromatic ring (59 → 60; 61, 63 → 62).

From a practical point of view the most important synthetic
methods starting from acyclic precursors are the following:

Compound	Name of synthesis	Section	Reaction type
Pyridines Dihydropyridines	Hantzsch	2.II.B.1.*b*	51 → 52
Piperidines, tetrahydropyrans	–	2.II.B.4	56 → 57
Quinolines substituted in the benzene ring	Skraup	2.II.C.2.*b*	59 → 60
Quinolines substituted in the pyridine ring	Friedlaender and Pfitzinger	2.II.C.1.*a.i* and *ii*	47 → 48
Quinolones	β-keto-ester	2.II.C.2.*a*	59 → 60
3,4-Dihydroisoquinolines	Bischler-Napieralski	2.II.D.*b.i*	61 → 62
Tetrahydroisoquinolines	Pictet-Spengler	2.II.D.*b.iii*	58 → 57
Isoquinolines	Pomeranz-Fritsch	2.II.D.*c*	63 → 62
Acridines	Bernthsen, etc.	2.II.C.2.*c.ii*	59 → 60
Phenanthridines	–	2.II.D.*b.iii*	61 → 62
Pyrones Thiopyrones	–	2.II.B.3	49 → 50
Pyrylium salts	–	2.II.B.2	47 → 48
Coumarins Chromones	Kostanecki-Robinson	2.II.C.1.*a.iv*	47 → 48
Chromones	Simonis	2.II.C.2.*a.ii*	59 → 60
Coumarins	von Pechmann	2.II.C.2.*a.ii*	59 → 60

Cross-references are also given here to methods of preparation of
these ring systems from other heterocyclic compounds.

Class of compound	Obtained indirectly starting from
Pyridines	Di- and tetra-hydropyridines (**2.V.A.***b*, **2.V.B.***a*) pyrroles (**4.III.C.1.***c.iv*)
Pyridinium salts	Pyridines (**2.III.B.3.***a*)
Pyridine 1-oxides	Pyridines (**2.III.B.5**)
Pyridones	Pyrones (**2.III.D.2.***c*), pyridines (**2.III.D.1.***a*), pyridine 1-oxides (**2.IV.B.1**), pyridinium compounds (**2.III.D.1.***b.i*), and halogeno- (**2.IV.A.5.***i*), amino- (**2.IV.A.7.***b.iv*) and alkoxypyridines (**2.IV.A.6.***a*)
Dipyridyls	Pyridine (**2.III.E.3**)
Dihydropyridines	Pyridines (**2.III.D.6**), pyridinium salts (**2.III.D.6**)
Tetrahydropyridines	Pyridines (**2.III.D.6**)
Piperidines	Pyridines (**2.III.D.6**)
Pyrones	Pyrylium salts (**2.III.D.1.***d*)
Pyrylium and benzopyrylium salts	Pyrones (**2.IV.A.6.***d.i*)
Quinolines	Dihydroquinolines (**2.V.A.***b*)
Isoquinolines	Dihydroisoquinolines (**2.V.A.***b*)
Carbolines	Indoles (**4.III.B.7.***d.iii*)

B. PREPARATION OF MONOCYLIC COMPOUNDS (PYRIDINES, PYRIDONES, PYRYLIUM SALTS, ETC.)

1. From Pentane-1,5-diones

(*a*) *General.* A pentane-1,5-dione (66) can undergo ring closure to give a pyran (69), or, in the presence of ammonia, a dihydropyridine

(67). Oxidative aromatization of these products occurs so easily (cf. Section **2.V.A.***b*) that it frequently takes place prior to isolation giving a pyrylium salt (70) or pyridine (68).

The pentane-1,5-dione is usually formed *in situ* by aldol- or Michael-type reactions (64 →65 → 66). Thus, acetaldehyde (64, R = H, R' = Me) and ammonia give 4-picoline and 3-ethyl-4-methylpyridine by formation of the intermediate (71), condensation with another molecule of CH_3CHO, and subsequent dehydrogenation. The same reaction also yields 2-picoline and 5-ethyl-2-methylpyridine *via* the intermediate (72).

(b) The Hantzsch Pyridine Synthesis. This is a special class of reactions of type (69) in which the methylene groups are further activated by ester groups and better yields are obtained. The simplest form of the Hantzsch synthesis involves the condensation of two molecules of a β-keto-ester with an aldehyde and ammonia (cf. 73 → 74).

Compounds resulting from the condensation of ammonia with one of the carbonyl components can be used in the Hantzsch synthesis. Thus β-aminocrotonic ester (75) can replace the ammonia and one mole of acetoacetic ester in (73).

2. From Pent-2-ene-1,5-diones

Ring closure of glutaconic dialdehyde (77) with the reagents indicated gives pyridine (76), pyridine 1-oxide (80), and the pyridinium (79) and pyrylium cations (78). Substituted glutaconic dialdehydes and related diketones react similarly. If one of the carbonyl groups is incorporated in a carboxyl group or a modified carboxyl group, α-pyridones and α-pyrones are formed.

Pent-2-ene-1,5-diones may be formed *in situ* (usually by an aldol-type reaction) and subsequently cyclized. Thus, malic acid (i.e.

hydroxy-succinic acid) with sulphuric acid gives carboxyacetaldehyde (81) which cyclizes spontaneously to coumalic acid (82).

The conversion of pyrylium cations into pyridines, pyridinium cations, and thiopyrylium cations, and of α-pyrones into α-pyridones, by ammonia, amines, and sulphide ions (see Section 2.III.D.2.*c*) involves open-chain intermediates of type (77).

3. From Pentane-1,3,5-triones

Ring closure of compounds of type (83) gives γ-pyrones (84, Z = O) by dehydration, and γ-pyridones (84, Z = NH) by the action of ammonia.

4. From Other 1,5-Disubstituted Pentanes

These methods often parallel syntheses used in the five-membered ring series (see Section 4.11.2.*a*). As indicated in structures (85)–(98), standard reactions of aliphatic chemistry can be extended to these preparations:

(*i*) Piperidines, tetrahydropyrans, and pentamethylenesulphides (87, Z = NH, O, S).

(*ii*) Δ^1-Tetrahydropyridines (92), and Δ^2-dihydro-pyrans and thiopyrans (93, Z = O, S).

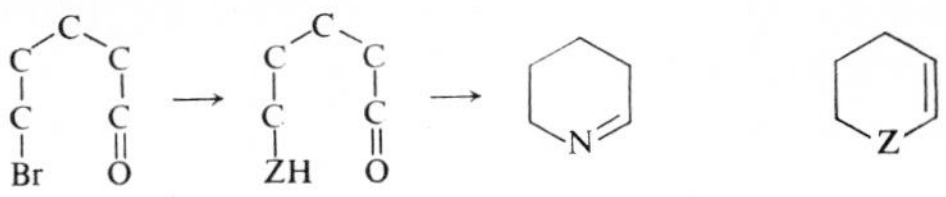

90   91   92   93

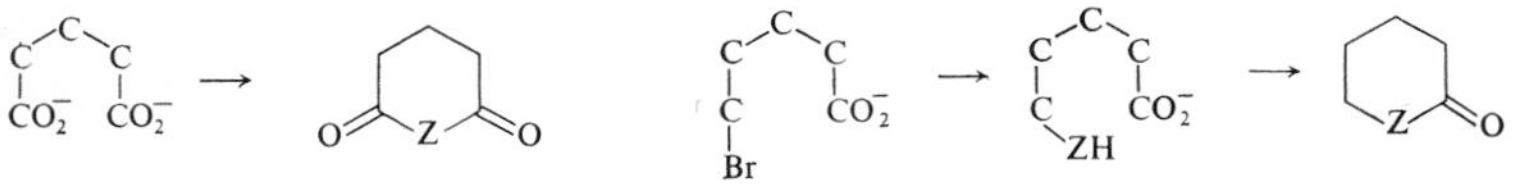

94   95   96   97   98

(*iii*) Glutarimides, glutaric anhydrides, and glutaric thioanhydrides (95, Z = NH, O, S).

(*iv*) δ-Lactams, δ-lactones, and δ-thiolactones (98, Z = NH, O, S).

5. Methods Involving C–C Bond Formation

Many of the standard methods of C—C bond formation in aliphatic systems can be extended to heterocyclic systems, e.g. the Dieckmann reaction (cf. 99 → 100) and alkylation of active methylene compounds.

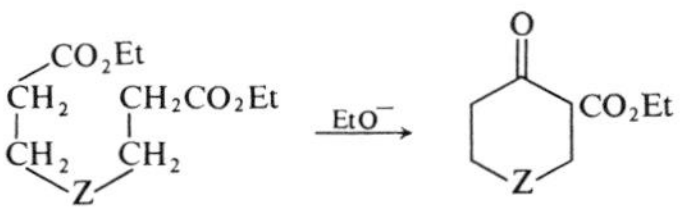

99   100

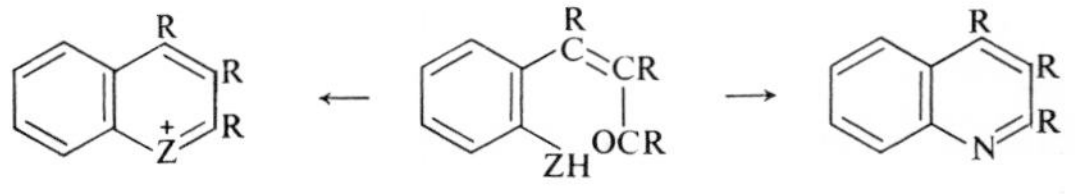

101   102   103

C. PREPARATION OF 2,3-BENZO DERIVATIVES (QUINOLINES, QUINOLONES, CHROMANS, ETC.)

1. Ring Closure of o-Substituted Anilines or Phenols

(*a*) *o-Substituted Cinnamoyl Derivatives.* o-Substituted benzenes of type (102, Z = O, S, NH) can undergo ring closure (102 → 101, 103). Amino derivatives (102, Z = NH), which usually cyclize spontaneously, are often prepared *in situ* by reduction of nitro compounds; e.g. o-nitrocinnamic acid with $(NH_4)_2S$ gives 2-quinolone.

Some important reactions involve an aldol reaction to form the intermediate (102) *in situ*.

(*i*) The Friedlaender synthesis of quinolines from *o*-aminobenzaldehydes and ketones (e.g. 104 → 105).

(*ii*) The Pfitzinger synthesis of quinoline-4-carboxylic acids from a ketone and isatinic acid, obtained *in situ* from isatin; e.g. (106) yields (107).

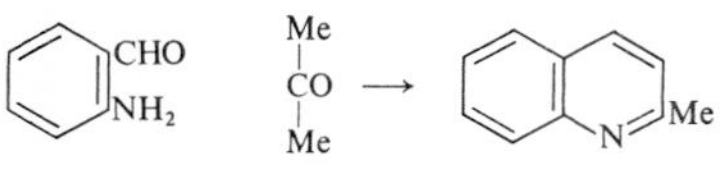

104   105 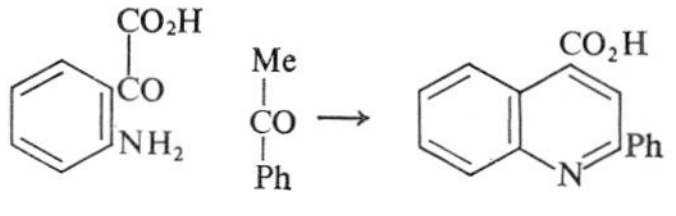   106   107

(*iii*) The preparation of benzopyrylium ions from ketones and *o*-acylphenols (109 → 108).

(*iv*) The Kostanecki-Robinson synthesis which can lead to coumarins (109 → 110) or chromones (111 → 112).

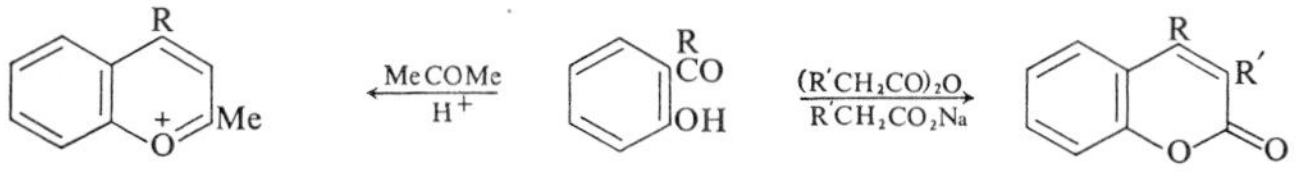

108   109   110

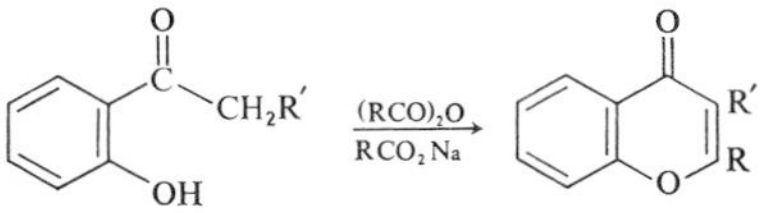

111   112 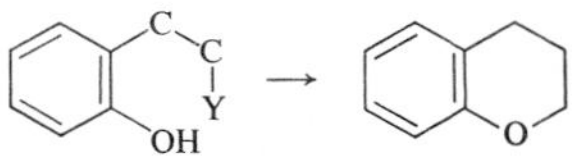   113   114

(*b*) *Other* o-*Substituted Benzenes.* Many standard reactions of aliphatic chemistry can be applied; for example, chromans (114) can be prepared by ring closure of (113, $Y = CH_2OH$), and flavanone (116) can be obtained by cyclization of (115).

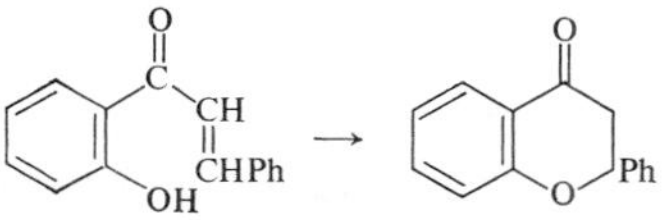

115   116 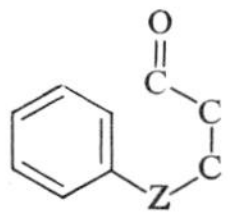   117

2. Formation of a C–C Bond by Reaction of a Carbonyl Group or Ethylenic Bond with a Benzene Ring

These reactions involve electrophilic attack on a benzene ring which is activated by the heteroatom (as in 117).

(*a*) *Quinolones and Benzopyrones*

(*i*) Anilines and β-keto-esters (118) give either Schiff's bases (121) or, on heating, the more slowly formed but more stable amides (119). Cyclization of the amide (119) yields 2-quinolone (120), whereas the Schiff's base (121) is converted into 4-quinolone (122) as shown.

(*ii*) Phenols and β-keto-esters (124) give either coumarins (123) (von Pechmann reaction) or chromones (125) (Simonis reaction) under the conditions indicated.

(*iii*) Thiophenols and β-keto-esters (with P_2O_5) give thiochromones.

(*b*) *Quinolines.* In the reactions tabulated opposite, Michael addition of a primary aromatic amine to an α,β-unsaturated aldehyde or ketone (prepared *in situ*) is followed by cyclization and oxidation of the intermediate dihydroquinoline to a quinoline (126 ⟶ 129).

Name of reaction	Starting materials	Catalyst	Intermediate carbonyl compound	Oxidizing agent
Skraup	glycerol	H_2SO_4	$CH_2:CH\cdot CHO$	As_2O_5, $m\text{-}NO_2\cdot C_6H_4\cdot SO_3H$, or nitro compound corresponding to the amine
Doebner-von Miller	RCHO and $R'CH_2CHO$	$ZnCl_2\text{--}HCl$	$RCH:CR'\cdot CHO$ ⎫	
Baeyer	RCHO and $R'CH_2COR$	HCl, 20°	$RCH:CR'\cdot COR$ ⎭	Schiff's base from RCHO and amine
Riehm	RCOR and $R'CH_2COR$	HCl, 200°	$\begin{matrix} R \diagdown \\ C:CR'\cdot COR \\ R \diagup \end{matrix}$	None (RH lost from product)*

(c) *Dibenzo Derivatives.* Reactions analogous to those given in Section 2.II.C.2.*a* lead to tricyclic compounds.

(*i*) *o*-Anilinobenzoic acids give 9-chloroacridines (131 → 130) and acridones (131 → 132).

(*ii*) In the Bernthsen synthesis, diphenylamines and carboxylic acids form 9-substituted acridines (133 → 135).

(*iii*) Phenanthridines are obtained by photochemical dehydrogenation of azomethines (136 → 137).

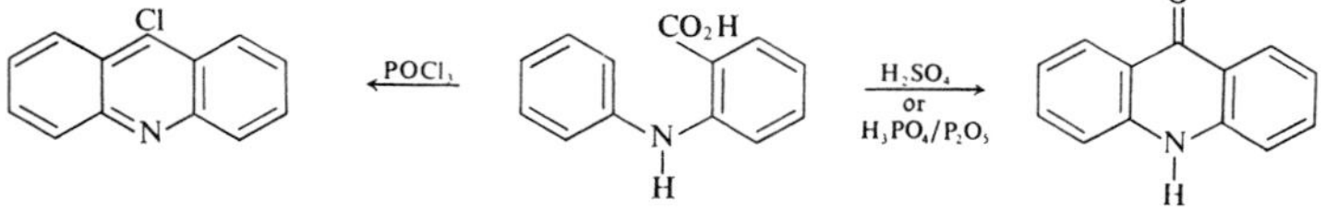

130   131   132

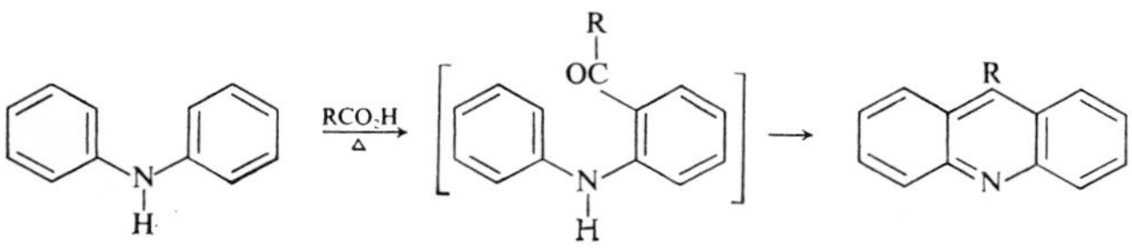

133   134   135

* Dihydroquinolines (e.g. 128, R = Me) can be isolated.

136   137

D. PREPARATION OF 3,4-BENZO DERIVATIVES (ISOQUINOLINES, ETC.)

(*a*) *Ring Closure of a Disubstituted Benzene*. Homophthalaldehyde (138) gives isoquinoline, isoquinoline 2-oxide, 3,4-benzopyrylium salts, and 2-alkyl- and 2-aryl-isoquinolinium salts (138 → 139) by reaction with NH_3, NH_2OH, H^+, or RNH_2, respectively.

138   139   140   141

(*b*) *From a β-Phenethylamine*. Condensation of the carbonyl group of an amide with a benzene ring forms the heterocyclic nucleus in the following cyclizations which are effected by acid catalysis (e.g. P_2O_5, $POCl_3$, H_3PO_4–P_2O_5):

(*i*) Bischler-Napieralski synthesis of 3,4-dihydroisoquinolines (141) from acylated 2-phenethylamines (140).

142   143

144   145   146

(*ii*) Pictet-Gams preparation of isoquinolines from N-acylated 2-hydroxyphenethylamines [e.g. (142) → papaverine (143)].

(*iii*) The preparation of phenanthridines from acylated 2-amino-biphenyls (144).

A Mannich-type reaction is used in the Pictet-Spengler synthesis of tetrahydroisoquinolines (145 → 146).

(*c*) *From a Benzylamine.* The most important condensation of type (147) is the Pomeranz-Fritsch synthesis of isoquinolines; e.g. $PhCHO + NH_2CH_2CH(OEt)_2$ at $100°$ → (148) → (149).

147   148   149

III. REACTIONS OF THE AROMATIC NUCLEI

A. GENERAL SURVEY OF REACTIVITY

In this section, the reactivity of each of the major types of aromatic rings is considered in comparison with that which would be expected on the basis of electronic theory, and the reactions of these hetero-aromatic systems are compared with similar reactions of aliphatic and benzenoid compounds. All the reactions quoted are dealt with in detail in subsequent sections.

1. Pyridines

(*a*) *Reactions of Electrophilic Reagents at the Annular Nitrogen Atom.* The lone pair of electrons on the nitrogen atom in trimethylamine and other tertiary amines reacts under mild conditions with electrophilic reagents:

(*i*) Proton acids give salts.

(*ii*) Lewis acids form coordination compounds.

(*iii*) Transition metal ions form complex ions.

(*iv*) Reactive halogen compounds give quaternary salts.

(*v*) Halogens form adducts.

(*vi*) Certain oxidizing agents yield amine oxides.

150   151   152   153

Pyridines react analogously with these electrophilic reagents at the lone electron pair on the nitrogen atom (150); see Section **2.III.B**.

(*b*) *Reactions of Electrophilic Reagents at a Ring Carbon.* Benzene reacts with electrophilic reagents under much more vigorous conditions, e.g. in nitration (NO_2^+), sulphonation (SO_3H^+), halogenation (ICl_3), and Friedel-Crafts reactions. Benzenes with an electron-withdrawing substituent (e.g. SO_3H or NO_2) undergo electrophilic substitution in the *m*-position only under still more vigorous conditions and some reactions, e.g. the Friedel-Crafts reaction, fail completely. Substitution of a nitrogen atom for a CH group in benzene is equivalent to introducing an electron-withdrawing group (nitrogen is more electronegative than carbon); thus, pyridine itself should be substituted in the 3-position (possibly about as readily as nitrobenzene). Substitution of a positively charged nitrogen atom for a CH group in benzene should, however, decrease the reactivity still further and pyridinium ions should be more resistant to reaction than pyridine. Electrophilic reagents react at the pyridine nitrogen atom very readily, and in the strongly acid media used for nitration, etc. conversion into the cation is essentially complete. Pyridines are therefore nitrated and sulphonated only with difficulty and at high temperatures; see Sections **2.III.C.1** and **2**. Halogenation of pyridines (see Section **2.III.C.3**) is easier, probably because reaction occurs on the free base. Dihalogenation occurs since a halogen atom causes little additional deactivation of the ring. The course of these reactions is illustrated by (151 $\rightarrow$ 152 $\rightarrow$ 153); pyridine is highly aromatic and therefore regains its original system of unsaturation. Determination of the resonance energies of heterocycles by combustion is difficult, but the most recent results indicate that the resonance energy of pyridine is slightly less than that of benzene.

(*c*) *Reactions of Nucleophilic Reagents at Ring Carbon Atoms.* The electron displacement toward the nitrogen atom allows nucleophilic reagents to attack pyridines at the α-position (154); benzene does not undergo this type of reaction. However, formation of the initial adduct (155) involves dearomatization of the pyridine ring and, once formed, the adduct tends to rearomatize by dissociation (155 $\rightarrow$ 154).

Only very strong nucleophilic reagents (e.g. NH_2^-, LiR, $LiAlH_4$, Na–NH_3, and, at high temperatures, OH^-) react appreciably (see Sections **2.III.D.1–5**). The tiny proportion of adducts of type (155) formed by addition of amide or hydroxide ions can also rearomatize by loss of a hydride ion, thus gradually causing complete reaction

(155 → 156). The adducts formed by the addition of hydride ions (from LiAlH$_4$) or carbanions (from LiR) are more stable; at low temperatures they are converted into dihydropyridines (157) by proton addition, but at higher temperatures rearomatization occurs by hydride ion loss.

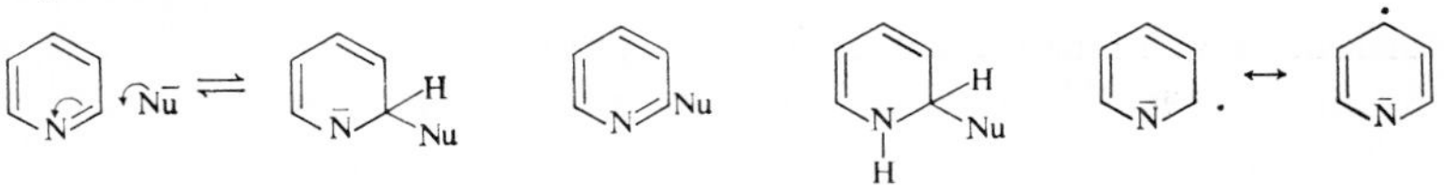

| 154 | 155 | 156 | 157 | 158 | 159 |

(*d*) *Free Radical Attack at a Ring Carbon Atom.* The following reaction types probably belong in this category:

(*i*) Aryl radicals attack unselectively at the α-, β-, and γ-positions just as in benzene chemistry.

(*ii*) Halogen atoms appear to react preferentially at the α-position.

(*iii*) Alkyl radicals attack the α- and γ-positions.

(*iv*) Certain metals (e.g. Na, Zn) add one electron to pyridine to form the ion-radical (158 ↔ 159) which can dimerize by reaction at the α- or γ-position, and the dimers form dipyridyls by hydride ion loss. These dimerizations are analogous to those of the ion-radicals R$_2$Ċ–O⁻ which are intermediates in the reduction of ketones to pinacols.

(*v*) Pyridines are reduced catalytically and chemically more easily than benzenes.

2. Pyridinium, Pyrylium, and Thiopyrylium Cation

(*a*) *Reaction with Electrophilic Reagents.* The positive charge prevents the reaction of electrophilic reagents at the heteroatom and strongly deactivates the ring carbon atoms. A rare example of electrophilic attack on a ring carbon atom is the nitration of 1,2,4,6-tetramethylpyridinium ion to give the corresponding 3-nitro derivative.

(*b*) *Reactions with Nucleophiles at a Ring Carbon.* The positive charge facilitates attack by nucleophilic reagents at positions α or γ to the heteroatom (e.g. 160). Hydroxide, alkoxide, sulphide, cyanide, and

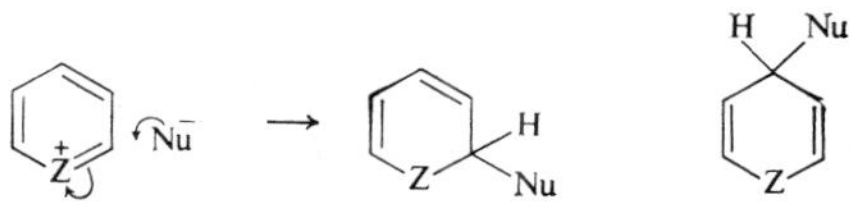

| 160 | 161 | 162 |

borohydride ions, certain carbanions, amines, and organometallic compounds react, usually at the α-position, under mild conditions to give initial adducts of types (161) and (162). These non-aromatic adducts can be isolated in certain cases but undergo further reactions with alacrity; the most important of these reactions include:

(*i*) Oxidation: (161, Nu = OH) ⟶ pyridones;
(161, Nu = CH_2·heterocycle) ⟶ cyanine dyes.

(*ii*) Disproportionation: (161, Nu = OH) ⟶ pyridone and dihydropyridine.

(*iii*) Ring opening with subsequent closure: reaction of pyrylium salts with RNH_2 or $S^=$.

(*iv*) Ring opening without subsequent closure: reaction of OH^- with pyridinium salts carrying electron-withdrawing groups on nitrogen and with pyrylium salts.

(*c*) *Reaction of Nucleophiles at a Hydrogen Atom.* Pyridinium cations have recently been shown to undergo ready hydrogen exchange at the α-position under mildly alkaline conditions; the reaction probably involves zwitterionic intermediates of type (163). The β- and γ-hydrogens exchange less readily.

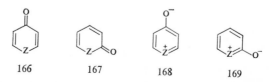

163   164   165

(*d*) *Reaction of Nucleophiles at an Annular Sulphur Atom.* Thiopyrylium salts react with aryl-lithium reagents to yield thiobenzenes (e.g. 164 ⟶ 165).

3. Pyridones, Pyrones, and Thiopyrones

(See also Section 2.IV.A.6.*d*.) These compounds are usually written in the unionized form (166, 167; Z = NH, NR, O, S), but canonical forms of types (168) or (169) are of comparable importance; i.e. the compounds can also be considered as betaines derived from pyridinium, pyrylium, and thiopyrylium cations. Their reactions follow logically from the possibilities of electron displacement in the molecules.

166   167   168   169

(*a*) *Electrophilic Reagents: Attack on a Ring Carbon Atom.* Electrophilic reagents (E^+) can attack ring carbon atoms β to the heteroatom as shown in (170) and (171); the intermediates (e.g. 172) usually revert to type by proton loss (172 $\longrightarrow$ 173). Halogenation takes place much more readily than it does in benzene. Nitration and sulphonation also occur, but in the strongly acidic environment required, the compounds are present mainly as unreactive cations (cf. reactions of type *b*).

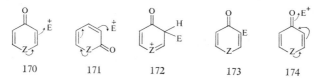

170   171   172   173   174

(*b*) *Electrophilic Reagents: Attack on a Carbonyl Oxygen Atom.* Electrophilic reagents can also attack the carbonyl oxygen atom (e.g. 174). Reactions of this type are considered under reactions of substituents (see Section **2.IV.A.6.***d*).

(*c*) *Nucleophilic Reagents: Removal of Proton from Ring Nitrogen Atom.* Nucleophilic reagents can remove a hydrogen atom on the heterocyclic nitrogen atom of pyridones (e.g. 175 $\longrightarrow$ 176). The resulting mesomeric anion (e.g. 176 $\leftrightarrow$ 177) reacts exceedingly readily with electrophilic reagents:
   (*i*) At nitrogen, e.g. with alkyl halides.
   (*ii*) At the β-carbon atoms, e.g. with CO_2.
   (*iii*) At oxygen, e.g. acylation (see Section **2.III.F.1**).

175   176   177   178   179   180

(*d*) *Nucleophilic Reagents: Attack at a Ring Carbon Atom.* Nucleophilic reagents can attack ring carbon atoms α or γ to the heteroatom (e.g. 178–180).
   (*i*) In both α- and γ-pyridones, the carbon atom of the carbonyl group can be attacked by a strong nucleophile (as in 178). The reaction then proceeds by complete loss of the carbonyl oxygen atom and subsequent aromatization. These reactions, which also

occur in α- and γ-pyrones, are all considered as substituent reactions in Section **2.IV.A.6.d.**

(*ii*) Adducts (178) formed by reaction of α-pyrones at the carbonyl carbon atom can react further by ring opening as in the reactions with hydroxide ion, ammonia, and amines (cf. Sections **2.III.D.1** and 2).

(*iii*) Nucleophilic attack at a ring carbon atom other than that of the carbonyl group can be followed by proton addition, i.e. by a Michael-type reaction. This is exemplified by the reaction of cyanide ions and carbanions at the γ-carbon atom of coumarins to give adducts of type (180) (see Section **2.III.D.5.c**).

(*iv*) γ-Pyrones react with hydroxide ions and amines at the α-carbon atom; the initial adducts (cf. 179) then undergo ring opening which is often followed by ring closure, e.g., to a pyridone (see Sections **2.III.D.1** and 2).

(*e*) *Free Radical Reactions* are of little importance, but pyridones and pyrones are easily reduced catalytically.

(*f*) α-*Pyrones* have relatively little aromatic character and can undergo Diels-Alder and other cyclic transition state reactions.

Thiones (e.g. 181) and onimines (e.g. 182) are relatively little known; they are mentioned in Sections **2.IV.A.7.a** and 8.a under substituent reactions.

181   182   183   184   185

4. N-Oxides

Pyridine 1-oxides, formally the betaines derived from 1-hydroxy-pyridinium cations, are worthy of separate consideration because of their unique pattern of reactivity.

(*a*) *Electrophilic Reagents* can attack the oxide oxygen atom (see substituent reactions, Section **2.IV.B**) and also the ring carbon atoms.

(*i*) N-Oxides in the free base form react with electrophiles in the 4-position (183); deprotonation of the Wheland intermediate results in 4-substitution, as in nitration.

(*ii*) N-Oxide cations react with electrophiles in the 3-position under forcing conditions. Sulphonation, which requires oleum, gives 3-pyridinesulphonic acid 1-oxide.

(*b*) *Strong Nucleophiles*, e.g. Grignard reagents, attack the α-carbon atom (184); the initial adduct loses a proton and an oxide ion to form the α-substituted deoxygenated heterocycle (185) (cf. Section **2.III.D.5.***a*). Hydrogen exchange also occurs under the influence of hydroxide ions, probably by proton loss (cf. Section **2.III.A.2.***c*).

(*c*) *Weaker Nucleophilic Reagents*, e.g. chloride, cyanide, and acetoxy ions, can attack the α- or γ-carbon only if the N-oxide first forms a coordinated intermediate with an electron acceptor (as in reactions with SO_2Cl_2, PhCOCl–KOH, and Ac_2O) (cf. Sections **2.III.D.4** and **2.IV.B.1**).

5. Effects of Substituents

(*a*) *Electrophilic Attack at Ring Nitrogen.* The ease of attack by electrophilic reagents at the nitrogen atom of pyridine depends on the electron density on that atom and the degree of steric hindrance.

(*i*) Strongly electron-withdrawing substituents (e.g. NO_2, COR, Cl) make these reactions more difficult by decreasing the electron density on the nitrogen atom; the effect is largely inductive and therefore is particularly strong from the α-position.

(*ii*) Strongly electron-donating substituents (e.g. NH_2, OR) facilitate electrophilic attack by increasing the electron density on the nitrogen; this is caused by the mesomeric effect and is therefore strongest from the α- and γ-positions.

(iii) Fused benzene rings, aryl and alkyl groups, and other groups with relatively weak electronic effects have little influence.

The foregoing effects are illustrated by the pK_a values given in Section **2.III.B.1.***b*. Reactions other than proton addition are hindered by all types of α-groups (cf. Sections **2.III.B.3–6**).

(*b*) *Electrophilic Attack at a Ring Carbon Atom.* The influence of substituent groups on the ease and orientation of electrophilic attack on ring carbon atoms can be largely predicted from a knowledge of benzene chemistry.

(*i*) Strongly electron-attracting substituents (e.g. NO_2, SO_3H, CO_2H) prevent these reactions in pyridines unless the ring is otherwise strongly activated. However, pyridones and pyrones carrying such a substituent will still react.

(*ii*) Strongly electron-donating groups (e.g. OH, NH_2, OR, NR_2)

greatly facilitate reaction, and pyridines containing one such group are nitrated and sulphonated (Sections **2.III.C.1** and 2) about as readily as benzene; mono- or di-substitution can be effected as shown (186–188).

186   187   188

m-Disubstituted benzenes containing one strongly *o-p*-directing and one strongly *m*-directing group are often further substituted between the two groups, and this may be compared with the orientation observed in (187).

Pyridines, pyridones, and pyrones containing an amino or hydroxyl group also undergo diazo-coupling, nitrosation, and Mannich reactions (Section **2.III.C.4**) just as their benzenoid analogues, phenol or aniline. These reactions take place under conditions of relatively low acidity where only small amounts of the compounds are in the form of unreactive cations.

(*iii*) Alkyl groups and halogen atoms behave normally as weakly activating and deactivating substituents, respective'y, and usually do not affect the orientation. Fused benzene rings effect the orientation of substitution, thus in benzo- and phenyl-pyridines and in phenylpyridine 1-oxides, electrophilic substitution most frequently occurs in the benzene ring. In benzo-pyridones, -pyrones, and -pyridine 1-oxides, electrophilic substitution can occur in either the benzene or the heterocyclic ring depending on the conditions (see Section **2.IV.A.*a***).

(*c*) *Nucleophilic Attack at a Ring Carbon Atom.* Nucleophilic attack on the ring carbon atoms of pyridines should be. and is, facilitated by electron-attracting substituents and hindered by electron-donating substituents. In pyridinium salts, the effect of strongly electron-withdrawing substituents attached to the nitrogen atom [e.g. $-C_6H_3(NO_2)_2$ or $-CN$] is particularly marked and causes ring opening (see Sections **2.III.D.1** and 2); this usually does not happen with other substituents.

Fused benzene rings aid nucleophilic attack on pyridines, pyridinium and pyrylium ions, and pyrones; the loss of aromaticity involved in the formation of the initial adduct is less in monobenzo derivatives and still less in linear dibenzo derivatives than in monocyclic compounds. For the same reason, the tendency for this initial adduct to rearomatize is less in benzopyridines. Fused benzene rings also influence the point of attack by nucleophilic reagents; attack rarely occurs on a carbon atom shared with a benzene ring. Thus, in linear dibenzo derivatives, nucleophilic attack is at the γ-position (189).

189

(d) *Free Radical Attack.* Substituents should have little effect on reactions involving free radicals, which are generally unselective; the available experimental evidence (Section 2.III.E) substantiates this view.

B. ELECTROPHILIC ATTACK AT THE PYRIDINE NITROGEN ATOM

Electrophilic attack at the pyridine nitrogen atom is considered in general terms in Section 2.III.A.1, and the effect of substituents in Section 2.III.A.5. The individual reaction types which are encountered are discussed here.

1. Proton Acids

(a) *Salt Formation.* Pyridines form stable salts with strong acids. Yellow ionic picrates are formed and are useful for characterization. Pyridine itself is often used to neutralize acid formed in a reaction and as a basic solvent. The basicity of pyridine (pK_a 5·2, as measured by the dissociation constant of its conjugate acid) is less than that of aliphatic amines (cf. NH_3, pK_a 9·5; NMe_3, pK_a 9·8). This reduced basicity is probably due to the changed bond hybridization of the nitrogen atom; in ammonia the lone electron pair is in an sp^3-orbital, but in pyridine it is in an sp^2-orbital. The higher the s character of an orbital, the more it is concentrated near the nucleus, and the less available it is for bond formation. Nitriles, where the lone electron pair is in an sp-orbital, are very weakly basic.

(b) *Substituent Effects.* The effects of representative substituents on the basicity of pyridine are shown in the table.

(*i*) Methyl groups are weakly base strengthening due to their inductive donor effect: α- and γ-methyl groups increase the pK_a somewhat more than do β-methyl groups.

(*ii*) Phenyl groups are weak resonance donors and acceptors, and inductive acceptors. The mesomeric effect does not operate for the *meta*-position, and 3-phenylpyridine has a basicity lower than that pKₐ VALUES FOR MONOSUBSTITUTED PYRIDINES*

	Me	*Ph*	*NH₂*	*OMe*	*Cl*	*CONH₂*
2-position	6·0	5·3	6·9	3·3	0·7	–
3-position	5·7	4·8	6·1	4·9	2·8	3·4
4-position	6·0	5·5	9·2	6·6	3·8	3·6

of pyridine, as expected. The inductive effect for the 4-position is weak, leading to an increased basicity, whereas the two effects cancel in 2-phenylpyridine.

(*iii*) Amino groups are strong resonance donors and hence base strengthening. The order of base strength is 4-amino > 2-amino (increased importance of the inductive effect) > 3-amino (small influence of the mesomeric effect).

(*iv*) Methoxy groups are resonance donors and inductive acceptors. The inductive effect is dominant for the 2-position, the mesomeric effect for the 4-position.

(*v*) Halogen atoms are inductive acceptors and weak resonance donors: they cause a marked decrease in basicity, especially from α-positions.

(*vi*) The carboxamido group is included in the table as an example of a resonance acceptor and inductive acceptor.

(*vii*) Fused benzene rings usually have little effect [cf. the pKₐ values of quinoline (4·85), isoquinoline (5·14), and acridine (5·6)]. Substituents on the benzene ring usually have little effect on the basicity.

2. Metal Ions

(*a*) *Simple Complexes.* Many transition and B-subgroup metals form complex ions with pyridines in aqueous solution; e.g. $Ni^{++} \longrightarrow Ni(C_5H_5N)_4^{++}$. If certain anions are also present, neutral complexes can result; e.g. $Cu^{++} + 2OCN^- + 2C_5H_5N \longrightarrow Cu(OCN)_2 \cdot (C_5H_5N)_2$.

(*b*) *Chelate Complexes.* Chelate rings can be formed by pyridines containing α-substituents such as carboxyl or $CH:NH$ groups. Important bicyclic chelating agents are 2,2'-bipyridyl (190, Y = H) and 8-hydroxyquinoline (191), which form *bis*- and *tris*-complexes with many metals. This type of complex formation has many analytical applications. Overlap between the *d*-orbitals of the metal atom and the pyridine π-orbitals is believed to increase the stability of many of these complexes. However, steric hindrance can prevent complex formation, as in (190, Y = Me).

* Determined in aqueous solution; cf. pyridine, pKₐ 5·2.

190   191

3. Reactive Halides and Related Compounds

(a) *Alkyl Halides, Etc.* Pyridines displace halide, sulphate, or sulphonate ions from primary and secondary alkyl halides, sulphates, and *p*-toluenesulphonates to form alkyl-pyridinium salts. These reactions are of the S_{N_2} type and are sensitive to steric changes in the pyridine or alkyl moieties. Pyridine reacts with methyl iodide or dimethyl sulphate on mixing, and heat is evolved. Reactions involving pyridines with α-substituents, or alkyl halides other than methyl, are slower and are often carried out by heating in a solvent of suitably high dielectric constant, such as acetonitrile, to promote ion formation.

Tertiary halides usually undergo bimolecular elimination on treatment with pyridines.

(b) *Aryl Halides.* Aryl halides react with pyridines only when they are highly activated. A familiar example is the reaction of 2,4-dinitrochlorobenzene with pyridine to give 1-(2,4-dinitrophenyl)-pyridinium chloride. To phenylate pyridine, a reagent much more reactive than phenyl chloride is required; such arylations have been accomplished with diaryliodonium ions ($Ph_2I^+BF_4^-$ + pyridine $\rightarrow$ 1-phenylpyridinium ion).

(c) *Acid Chlorides.* Acyl and sulphonyl halides and anhydrides react instantaneously with pyridine to form quaternary salts. These salts, which are not usually isolated, are excellent acylating and sulphonylating agents. The use of pyridine as a solvent in such reactions is a reflection of this.

4. Halogens

At room temperature pyridines react reversibly with halogens and interhalogens (e.g. ICl) to give unstable adducts. These adducts find some application as mild halogenating agents. X-ray diffraction studies of the pyridine-iodine complex have disclosed its structure to be (192).

5. Peracids

Pyridine 1-oxides are formed (193 $\rightarrow$ 194) by the treatment of pyridines with peracids. Typical conditions are $AcOH-H_2O_2$ at 100°

or $PhCO_3H$–$CHCl_3$ at 0°. The nitrogen atom in pyridine reacts less readily with peracids than does that in aliphatic triamines, which is consistent with expectation. Large α-substituents sterically hinder the reaction; thus, the N-oxidation of 2,6-diphenylpyridine proceeds in poor yield.

192   193   194   195

6. Other Lewis Acids

Pyridine readily forms stable coordination compounds. Thus boron, aluminium, and gallium trihalides react at 0° in an inert solvent to give 1:1-adducts (cf. 195). Steric factors are important, and α-substituents decrease the ease of reaction. This is illustrated by the heats of reaction of pyridine, 2-methylpyridine, and 2,6-dimethylpyridine with boron trifluoride which are 32·9, 31·2, and 25·4 kcal./mole, respectively. The marked decrease in exothermicity here should be contrasted with the small space requirements of the proton as shown by the pK_a values of substituted pyridines (cf. Section **2.III.B.1.***b*).

C. ELECTROPHILIC ATTACK AT THE RING CARBON ATOMS

In this section, the important electrophilic substitution reactions on all types of aromatic rings are systematically considered, attention having been given in Section **2.III.A.5** to general surveys of the reactivity of each major class of compound toward electrophilic substitution.

1. Nitration

(*a*) *Pyridines.* Pyridine itself requires vigorous conditions for nitration (H_2SO_4–SO_3–KNO_3 at 300°); 3-nitropyridine is obtained only in poor yield. A single methyl group evidently provides insufficient activation for nitration, since the picolines are extensively oxidized. However, 2,6-lutidine and 2,4,6-collidine afford the corresponding 3-nitro derivatives in fair yield under milder conditions (H_2SO_4–SO_3–HNO_3 at 100°).

As expected, an amino group greatly facilitates nitration. 2-, 3-, and 4-Aminopyridines are nitrated smoothly (H_2SO_4–HNO_3 at 40°) to form mono-nitro (5-, 2-, and 3-, respectively) and di-nitro derivatives (3,5-, 2,6-, and 3,5-, respectively) (cf. Section **2.III.A.5.*b*.**). Alkylamino-, alkoxyl-, and 3-hydroxy-pyridines react analogously to the corresponding amino compounds.

2,6-Dichloropyridine is nitrated under relatively mild conditions (100°) to give the 3-nitro derivative. This reaction occurs on the free base (in contrast to the nitrations mentioned above), the base weakening effect of the chlorine atoms allowing sufficient free base to be present at equilibrium for reaction to occur.

(*b*) *Pyridones.* 2- and 4-Pyridone and their 1-alkyl derivatives are readily nitrated to form first the 3-mono- (H_2SO_4–HNO_3, 30°) and then the 3,5-di-nitro derivatives.

(*c*) *Pyridine* 1-*Oxides.* Pyridine 1-oxide can be nitrated under reasonably mild conditions (H_2SO_4–HNO_3, 100°) to give the 4-nitro derivative in good yield. Substituted pyridine 1-oxides such as the 2- and 3-methyl, -halogeno, and -methoxyl derivatives also give the corresponding 4-nitro compounds in high yield. Quinoline 1-oxides are selectively nitrated in the 4-position at temperatures above *ca.* 80°, whereas at lower temperatures nitration occurs in the benzo ring (see Section **2.IV.A.2.*a*.**).

2. Sulphonation
Sulphonation of pyridine affords the 3-sulphonic acid in 70% yield, but vigorous conditions (H_2SO_4–SO_3, 230°) and mercuric sulphate, as catalyst, are required. The picolines similarly give *β*-sulphonic acids. 2-Aminopyridine and 1-methyl-2-pyridone are sulphonated under milder conditions (H_2SO_4–SO_3, 140°) in the 5-position.

Sulphonation of pyridine 1-oxide requires vigorous conditions (H_2SO_4–SO_3–Hg^{++}, 230°) and gives the 3-sulphonic acid (cf. Section **2.III.A.4.*a*.**).

3. Halogenation
Vapour phase chlorination (at 200°) and bromination (at 300°) of pyridine give fair yields of the 3-mono- and 3,5-di-halogeno derivatives. 3-Bromoquinoline and 4-bromoisoquinoline are formed under similar conditions, but nuclear substitution of alkyl-pyridines is precluded by preferential halogenation in the side chain (see Section **2. IV.A.3**).

Halogenation of 3-hydroxy- and 2-, 3-, and 4-amino-pyridines proceeds under milder conditions (e.g. Cl_2, Br_2, or I_2 in EtOH or H_2O, 20–100°) to form the mono- and di-halogeno derivatives. The orientations of these products is as expected, *ortho* and *para* to the activating group (see Section **2.III.A.5.**b).

2- and 4-Pyridones and 2- and 4-pyrones readily yield their 3-mono- and 3,5-di-halogeno derivatives; quinolones react similarly.

4. Nitrosation, Diazo-Coupling, and Reaction with Aldehydes

In general, only those pyridines containing hydroxyl or amino groups, and pyridones, will undergo these reactions. Some examples are:

(*i*) 3-Hydroxypyridine and formaldehyde give 2-hydroxymethyl-3-hydroxypyridine.

(*ii*) 2,6-Diaminopyridine with nitrous acid forms the 3-nitroso derivative.

(*iii*) 2-Pyridone (196) couples with diazonium salts to form azo compounds, which are also formed from 3-hydroxypyridines.

(*iv*) 4-Quinolone (197) undergoes Mannich reactions, e.g. with HCHO and $HNMe_2$ to form the 3-dimethylaminomethyl derivative.

196   197

5. Oxidation

It is convenient to discuss oxidative attack at ring carbon atoms here, although this can involve radical as well as electrophilic species. Pyridine rings are generally very resistant to oxidation: CrO_3 dissolved in pyridine is used as a reagent to oxidize hydroxyl groups, particularly in sterols. Many substituents on pyridine can be selectively oxidized by $KMnO_4$, O_2, or $K_2Cr_2O_7$, especially under acid conditions. In alkaline media, some oxidative degradation of the pyridine ring occurs; thus, isoquinoline gives both cinchomeronic (198) and phthalic acids ($KMnO_4$–NaOH–H_2O) (cf. Section **2.IV.A.2.**a). Ozone reacts with pyridines, although less readily than with benzenes; products corresponding to both Kekulé forms can be isolated (e.g. 200 → 199 + 201).

198   199   200   201

6. Acid-Catalyzed Hydrogen Exchange

Under vigorous conditions (H_2SO_4–H_2O, 200°), 2,4,6-collidine and 2,6-lutidine undergo acid-catalyzed hydrogen exchange at the β-ring positions. The 1,2,4,6-tetramethylpyridinium cation reacts under similar conditions.

D. NUCLEOPHILIC ATTACK AT THE RING CARBON ATOMS

The susceptibility of the various classes of aromatic rings towards nucleophilic attack is discussed in Section **2.III.A.3.***d*. Reactions of this type are now classified systematically.

1. Hydroxide Ion

(*a*) *Pyridine*. Uncharged pyridines are resistant to attack by hydroxide ions at temperatures up to 100°. Pyridine itself reacts with hydroxide ions under extreme conditions (KOH–air, 300°) to give 2-pyridone, the stable tautomer of 2-hydroxypyridine which is formed by oxidation of the initial adduct. As is expected, this reaction is facilitated by electron-withdrawing substituents and fused benzene rings; quinoline and isoquinoline react more readily than pyridine to give 2-quinolone and 1-isoquinolone, respectively.

(*b*) *Alkyl-Pyridinium Ions*. 1-Methylpyridinium ions (202) react reversibly with hydroxide ions to form a small proportion of the pseudo-base (203). The term 'pseudo' is used to designate bases that react with acids measurably slowly, not instantaneously as is normal for acid-base reactions. Fused benzene rings reduce the loss of resonance energy when the hetero ring loses its aromaticity, and hence pseudo-bases are formed somewhat more readily by 1-methylquinolinium, 2-methylisoquinolinium, and 10-methylphenanthridinium, and much more readily by 10-methylacridinium ions than by alkyl-pyridinium ions. Pseudo-bases carrying the hydroxyl group in

| 202 | 203 | 204 |

| 205 | 206 | 207 |

the α-position are usually formed preferentially, but acridinium ions react at the γ-position.

Pseudo-bases can undergo a number of further reactions:

(*i*) Oxidation. 1-Alkyl-pyridinium ions in alkaline solution are oxidized by $K_3Fe(CN)_6$ to give 2-pyridones (e.g. 204). 2-Quinolones, 1-isoquinolones, 6-phenanthridones, and 9-acridones can be prepared similarly.

(*ii*) Many pseudo-bases disproportionate on standing to dihydropyridines and pyridones (e.g., 205 → 206 + 207). The mechanism shown is speculative, but resembles that for the Cannizzaro reaction.

(*iii*) Ring fission, followed by closure to form a new heterocyclic or homocyclic ring, can occur in pyridinium ions carrying suitable substituents. Examples are: (208) + KOH + H_2O → (209) + EtOH, and, also under vigorous conditions, (210) + NaOH at 200° → 10% of (211).

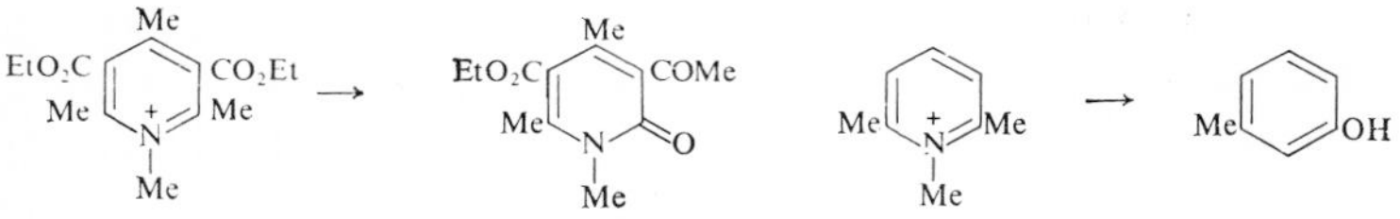

(*c*) *Other Pyridinium Ions.* Pyridinium ions carrying a strongly electron-withdrawing substituent on the nitrogen atom undergo ring fission by hydroxide ions under conditions ($NaOH-H_2O$, 20°) much milder than those required for fission of the 1-alkyl analogues. Pyridine-sulphur trioxide (212) and 1-cyanopyridinium ions give glutaconic dialdehyde (213 → 214); the other products are sulphamic acid and cyanamide (which decomposes to NH_3 and CO_2), respectively. Similarly, isoquinoline-sulphur trioxide gives homophthalaldehyde. These reactions can be considered to be the reverse of the synthetic method described in Section **2.II.B.2.**

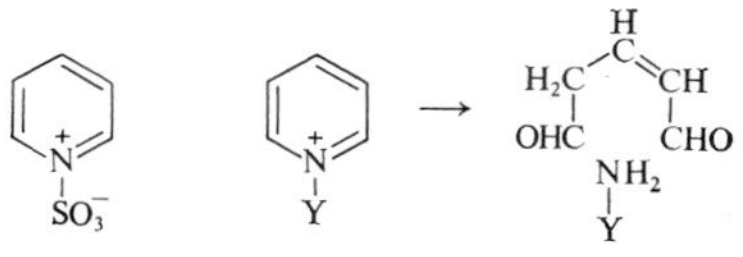

(*d*) *Pyrylium salts.* Pyrylium salts form pseudo-bases very easily. For example, the xanthylium ion (215) gives xanthydrol (216) which can be isolated or oxidized with dilute nitric acid to xanthone (217).

Ring opening follows in suitable cases; the pseudo-base (218) from 2,4,6-triphenylpyrylium ion is in equilibrium with the open-chain compound (219).

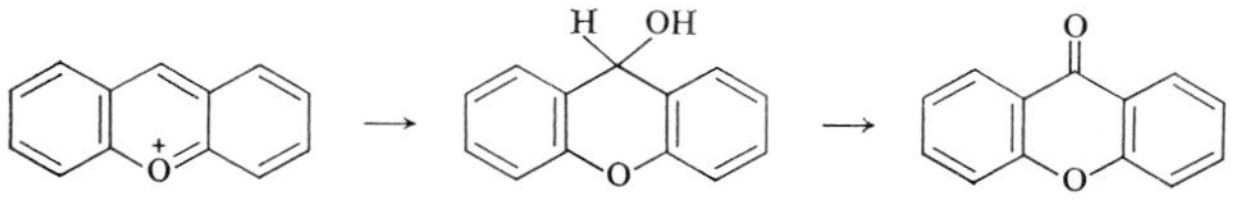

215   216   217

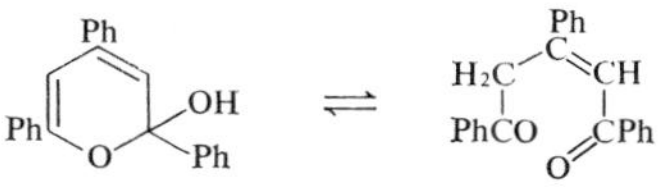

218   219

(*e*) *Pyrones.* Although pyridones are usually resistant to alkali, pyrone rings are often easily opened. In reactions of this type, hydroxide ions convert chromones into β-dicarbonyl compounds (e.g. 220 → 221) and coumarins reversibly into salts of coumarinic acids (e.g. 222 → 223).

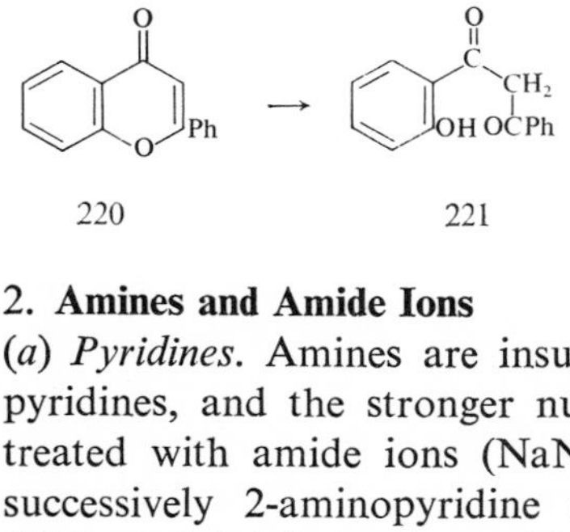

220   221 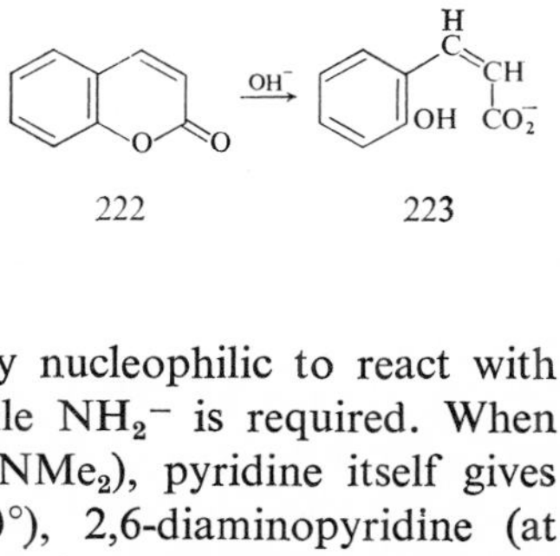   222   223

2. Amines and Amide Ions

(*a*) *Pyridines.* Amines are insufficiently nucleophilic to react with pyridines, and the stronger nucleophile NH$_2$⁻ is required. When treated with amide ions (NaNH$_2$–PhNMe$_2$), pyridine itself gives successively 2-aminopyridine (at 110°), 2,6-diaminopyridine (at 170°), and 2,4,6-triaminopyridine (at 200°, poor yield). The deactivating influence of electron-donating amino groups on subsequent stages of this reaction is evident.

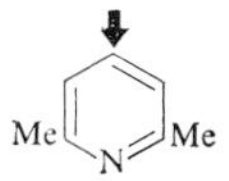

224 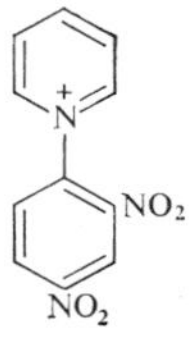   225 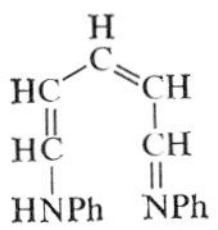   226

Amide ions react with substituted pyridines at an α-position unless both are blocked; thus, 2,6-lutidine (224), 2-methylquinoline, and acridine give γ-amino derivatives. Isoquinoline reacts in the 1-position. Methyl sodamide (Na^+NHMe^-) converts pyridine into its 2-methylamino derivative.

(*b*) *Pyridinium Ions.* The charged rings are sufficiently reactive to be attacked by amines. Pyridinium ions carrying strongly electron-withdrawing substituents on the nitrogen react to give open-chain products. Thus, 1-(2,4-dinitrophenyl)pyridinium ion (225) gives glutaconic dialdehyde dianil (226) and 2,4-dinitroaniline ($PhNH_2$, 100°) in the so-called Zinke reaction. Pyridine-sulphur trioxide (212) and 1-cyanopyridinium ion react similarly.

(*c*) *Pyrylium Ions.* Pyrylium cations form pyridines with ammonia and pyridinium salts with primary amines. For example, 2,4,6-triphenylpyrylium cation (227, Z = O) forms 2,4,6-triphenyl-pyridine with ammonia and the corresponding 1-methylpyridinium salt with methylamine. Xanthylium ions (215), where ring opening cannot readily occur, form adducts (228) with ammonia, amines, amides, ureas, sulphonamides, and imides. The last four classes of compounds can be converted into crystalline derivatives for character-ization in this way.

227   228   229   230

Monocyclic pyrones are converted into the corresponding pyri-dones, and isocoumarins into isoquinolones, by treatment with ammonia or primary amines [e.g. (229) → (230) with NH_3–H_2O at 100°].

3. Sulphide Ions
Pyrylium salts are converted by sodium sulphide into thiopyrylium salts [e.g. (227, Z = O) → (227, Z = S)]. This represents the only important synthesis of thiopyrylium salts.

4. Chloride Ions
Chloride ions are comparatively weak nucleophiles and do not react with pyridines. In general, there is also no interaction of chloride

ions with pyridinium and pyrylium compounds, but xanthylium chloride is in equilibrium with an appreciable amount of (231), this being a particularly favourable case with little loss of resonance energy on adduct formation.

Pyridine 1-oxides react with phosphorus oxychloride or sulphuryl chloride to form mixtures of the corresponding α- and γ-chloropyridines. The reaction sequence involves first formation of a nucleophilic complex (cf. 232), then attack of chloride ions on the complex, followed by rearomatization (see also Section **2.IV.B.1**) involving the loss of the N-oxide oxygen.

231   232

5. Carbanions

(a) *Organometallic Compounds.* Pyridine reacts with lithium alkyls and aryls under rather vigorous conditions (e.g. in xylene at 100°) to afford 2-alkyl- and 2-aryl-pyridines. The reaction proceeds *via* the corresponding dihydropyridines (233, or a tautomer), and these may be isolated at lower temperatures. The less reactive Grignard reagents give much poorer yields of these compounds.

Benzopyridines are attacked by organometallic compounds at an α-position unless both are blocked. The dihydro derivatives of quinolines and isoquinolines are more stable and less easily aromatized than are the dihydropyridines, and hence are more frequently isolated.

The corresponding reactions with N-oxides give α-substituted aromatic products by the loss of hydroxide ions from intermediates of type (234). However, the yields are poor because the N-oxide also acts as an oxidizing agent toward the organometallic compound.

233   234   235   236   237

Cationic rings react readily with organometallic compounds; thus, with a Grignard reagent, 1-methylquinolinium ions give products of type (235). A well-known reaction of this class is that of the pyridine-sulphur trioxide complex with sodium cyclopentadienide (236) to form azulene (237) by a sequence involving opening of the pyridinium ring and subsequent closure to the seven-membered carbocyclic ring.

(*b*) *Activated Methyl and Methylene Carbanions.* The mesomeric anions of activated methyl and methylene compounds react with pyridinium and pyrylium cations. Pyridinium ions combine with ketones (238) to give products of type (239) which can be isolated or oxidized *in situ* to mesomeric anhydro-bases (240) (cf. 327 ↔ 328). Quinolinium, isoquinolinium, and acridinium ions give similar adducts of stability increasing in the order given. Aliphatic nitro compounds react similarly; e.g. 1-methylquinolinium ion gives successively the adduct (241) and the anhydro-base (242) with CH_3NO_2–piperidine.

Pyrylium salts react with certain reactive methyl compounds by ring fission and subsequent cyclization to benzenoid products. 2,4,6-Triphenylpyrylium ion (243) in this way forms 2,4,6-triphenyl-nitrobenzene (244) with nitromethane and the substituted benzoic acid (245) with malonic acid; the latter reaction also involves a decarboxylation.

238   239   240   241   242

243   244   245   246   247

(*c*) *Cyanide Ions.* The so-called 'pseudo-cyanides', which are analogous to pseudo-bases, are formed by reaction of cyanide anions with benzopyridinium cations. Thus, 1-methylquinolinium ions give the pseudo-cyanide (246). The orientation of the addition is unusual in that attack occurs more often at the 2-position.

In the Reissert reaction, 1-benzoylquinolinium ions (formed *in situ* from quinolines and PhCOCl) and cyanide ions react to give 'Reissert compounds' [e.g. quinoline itself yields (247)]. These Reissert compounds are hydrolyzed by dilute alkali to quinoline-2-carboxylic acids and benzaldehyde.

6. Chemical Reduction

Pyridines are more susceptible to reduction than are benzenes. Treatment with sodium in ethanol or in liquid ammonia evidently reduces pyridine to 1,4-dihydropyridine (or a tautomer), because hydrolysis of the reaction mixture affords glutaconic dialdehyde $(250 \rightarrow 249 \rightarrow 248)$. Reduction of pyridines with sodium and ethanol can proceed past the dihydro stage to give Δ^3-tetrahydropyridines and piperidines $(250 \rightarrow 251, 252)$. Pyridine and lithium aluminium hydride form (253) which reacts with water to form 1,2-dihydropyridine (or a tautomer).

248   249   250   251   252   253

254   255   256   257   258

Cationic rings are readily reduced under relatively mild conditions. 1-Methylpyridinium ion with sodium borohydride (in H_2O at 15°) gives the 1,2-dihydro derivative (254) at pH > 7 and the 1,2,3,6-tetrahydro derivative (255) at pH 2–5. The tetrahydro compound is probably formed *via* (256), which results from proton addition to the dihydro derivative (254). Complex hydride reduction ($NaBH_4$ or $LiAlH_4$) of 1-methylquinolinium ions proceeds analogously to give 1,2-dihydro compounds (e.g. 257). Reduction of pyridinium ions with sodium hydrosulphite ($Na_2S_2O_4$–H_2O–Na_2CO_3) can give 1,4-dihydro products (e.g. 258).

E. FREE RADICAL ATTACK AT THE RING CARBON ATOMS

Free radical reactions are less important than those involving electrophilic or nucleophilic reagents. Only those reactions involving pyridine itself have been well studied.

1. Halogen Atoms

Vapour phase halogenation of pyridine at high temperatures gives mixtures of 2-mono- and 2,6-di-bromopyridine (Br_2, 500° or $CuBr-Br_2$, 350°) and 2-mono- and 2,6-di-chloropyridine (Cl_2, 270°). It is presumed that these reactions involve attack by free halogen atoms, in contrast to ionic halogenation which occurs at lower temperatures and gives β-substitution (cf. Section **2.III.A.1**). Under similar conditions (Br_2, 450°), quinoline gives 2-bromoquinoline.

2. Aryl Radicals

Phenyl radicals attack pyridine unselectively to form a mixture of 2-, 3-, and 4-phenylpyridines in proportions of *ca.* 53, 33, and 14%, respectively. The phenyl radicals may be prepared from the usual precursors: $PhN(NO)COCH_3$, $Pb(OCOPh)_4$, $(PhCO_2)_2$, or $PhI(OCOPh)_2$. Substituted phenyl radicals react similarly.

3. Dimerization Reactions

On treatment with sodium at 20°, pyridine forms mixtures of 2,2'-, 2,3'-, 2,4'-, and 4,4'-bipyridyl, probably by aromatization of intermediate dihydro compounds (e.g. 259 $\rightarrow$ 260). 2,2'-Bipyridyls (e.g. 260) also result from the reactions of pyridines with Raney nickel.

F. MISCELLANEOUS REACTIONS

This section collects together those reactions which cannot conveniently be classified under any of the previous headings.

1. Loss of a Proton from the Ring Nitrogen Atom

Pyridones are weak acids of pK_a *ca.* 11. They form mesomeric anions (cf. 261 $\rightarrow$ 262) which react very readily with electrophilic reagents at the nitrogen, oxygen, or carbon atoms, depending on

the conditions; see Section **2.III.A.3**. The anion (262) from 2-pyri-
done is alkylated or aminated on nitrogen (262 → 263, 264), acylated
on oxygen (262 → 265), and reacts at a ring carbon atom in the
Kolbe reaction (262 → 266). Attack on the pyridone anion (cf. 262)
is probably involved in certain other electrophilic substitutions [e.g.
the diazo-coupling of 4-quinolone (see Section **2.III.C.4**)].

2. Catalytic Hydrogenation

Pyridines are readily hydrogenated over Raney nickel at 120° to
give piperidines. Reductions with noble metal catalysts proceed
smoothly (at 20°) when the bases are in the form of their hydrochlorides; the free bases tend to poison the catalysts. A pyridine
ring is reduced more easily than a benzene ring; thus, 2-phenyl-
pyridine yields 2-phenylpiperidine (267), quinoline gives 1,2,3,4-
tetrahydroquinoline (268), and acridine affords 9,10-dihydroacridine
(269).

Pyridinium and pyrylium ions, pyridones, and pyrones are readily
hydrogenated; e.g. flavylium ion (270) and coumarin yield (271) and
(272), respectively.

3. Other Reactions

α-Pyrones show less aromatic character than pyridones or γ-pyrones and will undergo Diels-Alder reactions. With maleic ahydride, adducts of type (273) are formed; these adducts can lose carbon dioxide and react further with the anhydride to give (274).

273   274   275

276   277

Pyridine with acetylenedicarboxylic ester gives (275), (276), and other products. Quinoline and isoquinoline react similarly. Probably the initial product in each case is of type (277), formed by a Michael-type reaction. The initial product then reacts with another mole of acetylenic ester to yield the products observed.

IV. THE REACTIONS OF SUBSTITUENTS ATTACHED TO AROMATIC RINGS

In this section substituents attached to carbon and to nitrogen are considered separately because of their different character. Important synthetic routes to substituted derivatives are summarized in Section 2.IV.C.

A. SUBSTITUENTS ON CARBON

1. General Survey

If the reactions of the same substituents on heteroaromatic nuclei and on benzene rings are compared, the differences in the reactivities are a measure of the heteroatom's influence. For six-membered heteroaromatic rings, this influence is relatively small when the substituent is β to the heteroatom, but it is large for α- and γ-substituents.

(*a*) *Substituent Environment.* An α-substituent on pyridine (278) is in an electronic environment approaching that of a substituent on the corresponding imino compound (279). Since the reactions of the carbonyl compounds (280) are more familiar than those of the imino compounds (279), the reactions of α-substituted pyridines are perhaps best compared with those of the analogous carbonyl compounds. However, the electron-pull is much greater in carbonyl compounds than in pyridine; α-substituents on pyridine accordingly show reactivities intermediate between those of substituents on benzene and substituents attached to carbonyl groups. The electron-withdrawing effect of the annular nitrogen atom can be transmitted to the γ-position of pyridine (281) (illustrating the principle of vinylogy). Hence, γ-substituents have properties similar to those of α-substituents.

278   279   280   281   282   283   284

In pyridinium, pyrylium, and thiopyrylium ions (282), the electron-pull of the positively charged heteroatom is stronger than that in carbonyl compounds, and substituents attached to the α- or γ-positions of these cationic rings show correspondingly enhanced reactivity.

Pyridones, pyrones, thiopyrones, and N-oxides can act either as an electron source or as an electron sink depending on the requirements of the reaction (see discussion in Section **2.III.A.3**). It is usually found that substituents α or γ to the heteroatom in 2- and 4-pyridones, 2- and 4-pyrones, and 2- and 4-thiopyrones (e.g. 283), and pyridine 1-oxides (284) are activated by electron-withdrawal much as they are in pyridine itself.

β-Substituents cannot conjugate with the heteroatom and therefore usually react as they would on a benzene ring (see, however, Sections **2.IV.A.3 and 5**).

(*b*) *The Carbonyl Analogy.* Substituent reactions are often modified to a large extent by an adjacent carbonyl group. As would be expected from the discussion in the preceeding section, the reactions of α- and γ-substituents on six-membered heterocyclic rings are similarly influenced by the heteroatom. The various effects on substituents can be classified into six groups (*i–vi*). Examples of these effects are given for both carbonyl and heterocyclic compounds in the table.

(*i*) Groups which can form anions are readily displaced by nucleophilic reagents (285).

(*ii*) α'-Hydrogen atoms are easily lost as protons (286).

(*iii*) As a consequence of (*ii*), tautomerism is possible (287 ⇌ 288).

(*iv*) Carbon dioxide is readily lost from carboxymethyl (289) and carboxyl groups (290).

(*v*) These effects are transferred through a vinyl group, and nucleophilic reagents will add to vinyl and ethynyl groups (291) (Michael reaction).

(*vi*) Electrons are withdrawn from aryl groups (292).

Reaction type	Group	α- or γ-Groups in pyridine	See section	Compare with
Nucleophilic displacement	Nitro	Are displaced readily	2.IV.A.7.*e*	–
	Halogen	Are displaced	2.IV.A.5	Acid chloride
	Alkoxyl ⎱	Are displaced when additionally activated ⎰	2.IV.A.6.*a*	Ester
	Amino ⎰		2.IV.A.7.*a*	Amide
Proton loss	Hydroxyl	Are acidic	2.IV.A.6.*b*	Carboxylic acid
	Amino	Are less basic	2.IV.A.7.*a*	Amide
	Alkyl	Become 'active'	2.IV.A.6.*a*	Ketone
Tautomerism	Hydroxyl	Exist *ca.* 99·9% in the one-form	2.IV.A.6.*c*	Carboxylic acid (two equivalent structures)
	Amino	Exist *ca.* 0·1% in the onimine-form	2.IV.A.7.*a*	Amide
	Mercapto	Exist *ca.* 99·99% in the thione-form	2.IV.A.8.*a*	Thiocarboxylic acid
Decarboxylation	Carboxyl	Decarboxylate at *ca.* 200°	2.IV.A.4.*a*	α-Keto-acids
	Carboxymethyl	Decarboxylate at *ca.* 50°	2.IV.A.4.*a*	β-Keto-acids
Michael reactions	Vinyl ⎱ Ethynyl ⎰	Undergo Michael additions readily	2.IV.A.4.*c*	α,β-Unsaturated ketones
	β-Hydroxyethyl	Undergo reverse Michael reaction readily (lose H_2O)	2.IV.A.6.*b*	β-Hydroxyketones
Electrophilic attack on phenyl groups	Phenyl	Undergo electrophilic substitution in the *meta* and *para* positions (*ca.* 1 : 1)	2.IV.A.2.*b*	Phenyl ketones

285 286 287 288

289 290 291 292 293

(c) *The Effect of One Substituent on the Reactivity of Another* is generally of secondary importance and similar to that observed in polysubstituted benzenes.

As in naphthalene, a fused benzene ring induces bond fixation. Hence, whereas substituents in the 1-position of isoquinoline (293, note numbering) behave like substituents in the 2-position of the pyridine nucleus, substituents in the 3-position of isoquinoline show a reactivity less than that of true α-substituents and about midway between those of 2- and 3-substituents on pyridine.

(d) *Reactions of Substituents Not Directly Attached to the Heterocyclic Ring.* In general, substituents removed from the ring by two or more saturated carbon atoms undergo normal aliphatic reactions. A notable exception is the reversed Michael reaction of β′-substituted ethyl compounds (see Section 2.IV.A.6.c).

Substituents attached directly to fused benzene rings or aryl groups undergo the same reactions as those on normal benzenoid rings. Naturally, a substituent on the benzenoid ring in quinoline or isoquinoline is better compared with that on a naphthalene rather than with that on a benzene nucleus; e.g., hydroxy derivatives of this type undergo the Bucherer reaction [ArOH + $(NH_4)_2SO_3 \rightarrow ArNH_2$] which is typical for naphthols.

2. Benzenoid Rings
(a) *Fused Benzene Rings.*
   (i) *Unsubstituted Benzenoid Rings.* In compounds with fused benzene rings, electrophilic substitution on carbon usually occurs in the benzenoid rings in preference to the heterocyclic ring. Frequently the orientation of substitution in these compounds parallels that in naphthalene. Nitration (H_2SO_4–HNO_3, O°) of quinoline and

isoquinoline occurs in positions corresponding to the α-positions in naphthalene, as shown in diagrams (294) and (295). Sulphonation of quinoline and isoquinoline (H_2SO_4–SO_3) is temperature-dependent (100–300°) and yields 5-, 6-, 7-, and 8-quinolinesulphonic acids and 5-, 7-(?), and 8-isoquinolinesulphonic acids, again showing the resemblance to naphthalene.

Vigorous oxidation (e.g. with $KMnO_4$) usually degrades fused benzene rings in preference to pyridine rings, especially under acid conditions. Quinoline and isoquinoline yield the pyridinedicarboxylic acids (296) and (297), respectively. Oxidation of a fused benzene ring is facilitated when it carries electron-donating groups and is hindered by electron-withdrawing substituents. Ozonolysis of quinoline gives glyoxal and 2,3-pyridinedicarboxaldehyde.

294   295   296   297

(*ii*) Substituted Benzenoid Rings. Substituents on the benzene rings exert their usual influence on the orientation and ease of electrophilic substitution reactions. For example, further nitration (H_2SO_4–SO_3–HNO_3) of 5- and 8-nitroquinolines occurs *meta* to the nitro group as shown in diagrams (298) and (299). Friedel-Crafts acylation of 8-methoxyquinoline is successful (cf. 300), but this reaction fails with quinoline itself.

A heterocyclic ring induces partial double-bond fixation in a fused

298   299   300

301   302

benzene ring. Hence, diazo-coupling occurs at the 5-position of 6-hydroxyquinoline (301), and not at the 7-position.

(*b*) *Aryl Groups.* Electrophilic substitution usually occurs preferentially in the aryl group. Indeed, in compounds containing both an aryl group and a fused benzene ring, electrophiles usually attack the aryl group exclusively. Nitration of α- and γ-phenylpyridines gives mixtures of the *o*-, *m*-, and *p*-nitrophenyl derivatives (cf. 302); this is a good illustration of reactivity midway between that of the corresponding carbonyl and benzenoid derivatives. Acetophenone is nitrated mainly in the *meta*-position, biphenyl exclusively in the *ortho*- and *para*-positions.

3. Alkyl Groups

(*a*) *Alkyl Groups Attached to Heteroaromatic Systems* undergo many of the same reactions as those on benzenoid rings:

(*i*) Oxidation in solution ($KMnO_4$, CrO_3, etc.) gives the corresponding carboxylic acid or ketone [e.g. 3-picoline $\longrightarrow$ nicotinic acid (303), and 2-benzylpyridine $\longrightarrow$ 2-benzoylpyridine (304)].

(*ii*) Controlled catalytic vapour phase oxidation converts 2-, 3-, and 4-picolines into 2-, 3-, and 4-pyridinecarboxaldehydes, respectively.

(*iii*) Free radical bromination with N-bromosuccinimide succeeds [e.g. 2,6-dimethyl-4-pyrone yields the bromo derivative (305)].

| 303 | 304 | 305 |

(*b*) α- *and* γ-*Alkylpyridines.* In addition to the reactions described in the preceding sections, alkyl groups in the α- and γ-positions of pyridine rings show reactions which result from the easy loss of a proton from the carbon atom of the alkyl group which is adjacent to the ring (see Section 2·IV.A.1).

The strongest bases, such as sodamide ($NaNH_2$–NH_3, −40°) or organometallic compounds (PhLi–Et_2O, 40°), convert 2- and 4-alkylpyridines essentially completely into the corresponding anions (e.g. 306). These anions react readily even with mild electrophilic reagents (as 307), thus the original alkyl groups can be substituted in the following ways:

(*i*) Alkylation [e.g. 2-picoline (308) gives 2-*n*-propylpyridine (309)].

(*ii*) Acylation [e.g. lepidine (310) yields 4-phenacylquinoline (311)].

(*iii*) Carboxylation [e.g. 2-picoline (308) affords 2-pyridineacetic acid (312), which must be esterified before isolation (see Section **2.IV.A.4.a**)].

(*iv*) Reaction with carbonyl compounds to form alcohols [e.g. 2-picoline (308) yields the tertiary alcohol (313)].

The methyl group of 3-picoline is sufficiently reactive to be alkylated and acylated in this way, although the yields are poor.

In aqueous or alcoholic solution, 2- and 4-alkyl-pyridines react with bases to give traces of anions of type (306). With suitable electrophilic reagents, these anions undergo reasonably rapid and essentially non-reversible reaction. Such reactions are illustrated using 4-picoline (315) and quinaldine (319) as typical substrates:

(*i*) Formaldehyde gives poly-alcohols (315 → 317).

(*ii*) Aliphatic aldehydes (other than HCHO) form mono-alcohols (315 → 316).

(*iii*) Aromatic aldehydes give styryl derivatives (315 → 314) by spontaneous dehydration of the intermediate alcohol (cf. Section **2.IV.A.6.c**).

(*iv*) Halogens displace all adjacent hydrogen atoms (319 → 318).

(*v*) Formaldehyde in the presence of amines yields Mannich bases (319 → 320).

These reactions can be catalyzed by alkoxide or hydroxide ions, amines, or the alkyl-pyridine itself. Alternatively, an acid-type catalyst such as acetic anhydride may be used; the acid-type catalyst forms a complex of type (321) from which proton loss is facile.

(*c*) *Alkyl-Pyridine 1-Oxides and -Pyridones.* α- and γ-Alkyl groups on pyridine 1-oxides are somewhat more reactive than those on pyridines. In addition to the reactions summarized in the preceding paragraph, 2-picoline 1-oxide undergoes Claisen condensation with ethyl oxalate to yield the pyruvic ester (322).

α- and γ-Alkyl groups on pyrones and pyridones also undergo many reactions of the types described in the preceding section. For example, with benzaldehyde, 2,6-dimethylpyrone gives the styryl derivative (323).

(*d*) *Alkyl-Pyridinium and -Pyrylium Compounds.* Proton loss from α- and γ-alkyl groups on a cationic (pyridinium or pyrylium) ring is comparatively easy. The resulting neutral anhydro-bases or 'pyridone methides' (cf. 324) can be isolated using 10N-sodium hydroxide. These anhydro-bases react readily with electrophilic reagents to give products which can often lose a proton to give new resonance-stabilized anhydro-bases. Thus, anhydro-1,2-dimethylpyridinium hydroxide (324) reacts with phenyl isocyanate to give an adduct (326) which is converted into the stabilized product (327 ↔ 328). By a similar reaction with carbon disulphide, (324) yields the dithio acid (325).

α- and γ-Alkyl-cationic heterocycles, analogously to the 2- and 4-alkyl-pyridines, can also react with electrophilic reagents without initial complete deprotonation. They undergo the same types of reactions as the alkyl-pyridines under milder conditions, and these reactions are often catalyzed by piperidine (e.g. 329 → 330).

Some weak electrophilic reagents, which are usually inert toward pyridines, also react. Diazonium salts yield phenylhydrazones (e.g. 331 → 332, Z = NMe, O) in a reaction analogous to the Japp-Klingemann transformation of β-keto-esters into phenylhydrazones. Cyanine dye preparations fall under this heading. Monomethine cyanines are formed by reaction with an iodo-quaternary salt [e.g. (333) + (334) → (335; $n = 0$)]. Tri- and penta-carbocyanines (335, $n = 1$ and 2, respectively) are obtained by the reaction of two molecules of a quaternary salt with one molecule of ethyl orthoformate (336, $n = 0$) or β-ethoxyacrolein acetal (336, $n = 1$), respectively.

(*e*) *Tautomerism of Alkyl-Pyridines.* Analogous to the tautomerism of the hydroxy- and amino-pyridines (cf. Sections **2.IV.A.6.**c and **7.**a), there are alternative tautomeric alkylidene forms of the 2- and 4-alkyl-pyridines (e.g. 337 for 2-picoline). However, since only a small proportion of the amino-pyridines exists in the imino form, the alkylidene form should be even less important (cf. argument in Section **2.IV.A.7.**a). For simple alkyl compounds, basicity considerations (cf. Section **7.**4) suggest that at equilibrium only one part in about 10^{11} exists in the alkylidene form.

4. Other Carbon-Containing Functional Groups

(*a*) *Carboxylic Acids.* Pyridinecarboxylic acids are amino-acids and consequently exist partly in the zwitterionic, or betaine form (338).

Pyridinecarboxylic acids decarboxylate on heating with increasing ease in the order $\beta << \gamma < \alpha$. Pyrone- and pyridone-carboxylic acids also decarboxylate readily. The relatively easy decarboxylation of α- and γ-carboxylic acids is a result of inductive stabilization of intermediate ions of type (339) (cf. Section **2.IV.A.1**); their existence can be confirmed by carrying out the decarboxylation in the presence of aldehydes or ketones when products of type (340) are formed (Hammick reaction).

338   339   340

341   342   343   344

Pyridines with an α- or γ-carboxymethyl group (e.g. 341) undergo facile decarboxylation by a mechanism (341 → 342) similar to that for the decarboxylation of β-keto-acids (cf. Section **2.IV.A.1**). Carboxymethylpyridines often decarboxylate spontaneously; thus, hydrolysis of (343) gives (344). 3-Pyridineacetic acid shows no tendency to decarboxylate.

In most other reactions, the pyridinecarboxylic acids and their derivatives behave as expected (cf. schematic diagram); however, some acid chlorides can be obtained only as hydrochlorides.

Py' $\xrightarrow{\text{PhH}}$ PyPh   PyCOMe $\xrightarrow{\text{Willgerodt}}$ PyCH$_2$CO$_2$H

$\uparrow \Delta$

(PyCO$_2$)$_2$ (PyCO)$_2$O   PyCOCH$_2$CO$_2$Et   PyCH$_2$OH

Na$_2$O$_2$ PyCO$_2$Na   NaOEt EtOAc   LiAlH$_4$

PyCOCl $\xleftarrow{\text{SOCl}_2}$ PyCO$_2$H $\xrightarrow[\text{EtOH}]{\text{H}_2\text{SO}_4}$ PyCO$_2$Et $\xrightarrow{\text{N}_2\text{H}_4}$ PyCON$_2$H$_3$

PhH—AlCl$_3$ H$^+$or OH$^-$ NH$_3$ HNO$_2$, Δ

PyCOPh   PyCN $\xleftarrow{\text{SOCl}_2}$ PyCONH$_2$ $\xrightarrow{\text{NaOCl}}$ PyNH$_2$

(Py represents 2-, 3-,or 4-pyridyl)

(*b*) *Aldehydes and Ketones.* In general, the properties of these compounds and those of their benzenoid analogues are similar. Aldehyde groups α to the heteroatom undergo the benzoin condensation very readily because the end-products are stabilized as hydrogen-bonded ene-diols (e.g. 345).

345   346

(*c*) *Vinyl and Ethynyl Groups.* Vinyl groups α or γ to the pyridine nitrogen atom readily undergo Michael additions. Water, alcohols, ammonia, amines, and hydrogen cyanide are examples of nucleophiles which may be added. For example, 2-vinylpyridine and dimethylamine give the adduct (346). The orientations of these Michael additions are as expected (cf. Section 2.IV.A.1).

The usual olefinic reactions are also shown by these groups.

5. Halogen Atoms
Nucleophilic replacement of an α- or γ-halogen atom is facilitated by mesomeric stabilization of the transition state (cf. acid halides, and see Section 2.IV.A.1). The reactions of 2-bromopyridine are

typical and are given in some detail. The bromine atom can be replaced by the following groups under the conditions indicated:

(*i*) Hydroxyl,* by NaOH–H_2O, 150°.

(*ii*) Alkoxyl, e.g. methoxyl, by NaOMe–MeOH, 65°.

(*iii*) Phenoxyl, by PhONa–EtOH.

(*iv*) Mercapto, by KSH–propylene glycol.

(*v*) Methylmercapto, by NaSMe–MeOH, 65°.

(*vi*) Amino (NH$_3$–H_2O, 200°) or dimethylamino (NHMe$_2$, 150°).

(*vii*) Cyano, by distillation with CuCN.

(*viii*) Di(ethoxycarbonyl)methyl, by the sodio derivative of malonic ester.

The relative reactivities with respect to nucleophilic displacement increase in the order Cl < Br < I; fluoro compounds have been little studied. The reactions of the 4-halogeno-pyridines parallel those of the corresponding 2-isomers, with the exception that 4-halogeno-pyridines polymerize much more readily (e.g. to 347) because the pyridine nitrogen atom is not sterically hindered and is more basic (cf. Section 2.III.B.2).

α- and γ-Halogen atoms on benzo-pyridines, -pyridones, -pyrones (e.g. 348), and N-oxides (e.g. 349) are about as reactive as those on pyridine itself. Halogen atoms in the α- and γ-positions of cationic nuclei are very reactive, as is illustrated by the hydrolysis of 2,6-dibromo-1-methylpyridinium ion at 20° (350 → 351).

347   350   351

β-Halogeno-pyridines are less reactive towards nucleophilic substitution than the α- and γ-isomers, but distinctly more reactive than unactivated phenyl halides. Thus, a bromine atom in the 3-position of pyridine or quinoline can be replaced by methoxyl (NaOMe–MeOH, 150°) or amino groups (NH$_3$–H_2O–CuSO$_4$, 160°).

* The products tautomerize to an alternative form (see Sections **2.IV.A.6.*c*** and **2.IV.A.8.*a***).

Some reactions of this type have been shown to involve pyridynes (cf. 352), formed by initial loss of hydrogen halide.

Just as in benzene chemistry, all types of halogen atoms are activated towards nucleophilic displacement by the presence of other electron-withdrawing substituents. This is illustrated by the conversion of 2-chloro-5-nitropyridine (354) into the 2-hydrazino (353) and the 2-oxo or 2-thioxo derivatives (355; Y = O or S) under the relatively mild conditions indicated.

352   353   354   355

Nuclear halogen atoms also show many of the reactions typical of aryl halogens.

(*i*) They can be replaced with hydrogen atoms by catalytic (Pd, Ni, etc.) or chemical reduction (HI or Zn–H_2SO_4).

(*ii*) They react to give Grignard reagents which show the normal reactions. However, in the preparation of such Grignard reagents, it is usually necessary to add ethyl bromide to activate the magnesium ('entrainment method').

(*iii*) Ullmann reactions succeed [e.g. 2-bromopyridine yields 2,2′-bipyridyl (with Cu)].

6. Oxygen-Containing Functional Groups

(*a*) *Alkoxyl Groups.* α- and γ-Alkoxyl-pyridines should be compared with esters. These alkoxyl groups undergo nucleophilic replacement when they are additionally activated by another substituent, as is the case for 4-methoxy-3-nitropyridine (356 → 357). Nucleophilic displacement of alkoxyl groups on cationic rings occurs exceedingly readily [e.g. 4-methoxy-2,6-dimethylpyrylium cation (359) yields (358) or (360)].

356   357

358   359   360

Pyridine and benzopyridines with alkoxyl groups in the α- or γ-position rearrange to N-alkyl-2- and -4-pyridones on heating. 2-Methoxypyridine gives 1-methyl-2-pyridone at 300°, whereas 2-methoxyquinoline forms the 2-quinolone at 100°. One molecule of the alkoxyl compound acts as an alkylating agent for another in these intermolecular reactions.

(*b*) *Acyloxy Groups*. On the carbonyl analogy, acyloxy-pyridines should be compared with acid anhydrides. Accordingly, 2- and 4-acyloxy derivatives are good acylating reagents; indeed they are difficult to isolate because of their ease of hydrolysis. Phosphoric esters of type (361) are useful phosphorylating reagents.

(*c*) *Hydroxyl Groups*. Hydroxypyridines (362) are weak acids of the phenol type and also bases and can therefore exist as zwitterions (363). The zwitterions of 2- and 4-hydroxypyridines are known as 2- and 4-pyridones because their uncharged canonical forms (e.g. 364 and 365) are the predominating species in aqueous solution (see Sections **2.III.A.3** and **2.IV.A.6.*d***). Physical measurements show that for α- and γ-hydroxypyridines only one part in *ca.* 10^3 is in the hydroxypyridine form in aqueous solution.

361	362	363	364	365

366	367

In aqueous solution the hydroxy and zwitterionic forms of β-hydroxypyridines coexist in comparable amounts. 3-Hydroxypyridine behaves as a typical phenol. It gives an intense violet colour with ferric chloride and forms a salt (366) with sodium hydroxide which can be alkylated by alkyl halides (to give 367, Y = alkyl) and acylated by acid chlorides (to give 367, Y = acyl).

Hydroxypyridine 1-oxides are also tautomeric; the 4-isomer exists in about equal amounts of forms (368) and (369). Hydroxy-pyrones and -pyridones exhibit a different type of tautomerism; the α-one structure (e.g. 370) is favoured relative to the γ-one structure (371).

368   369   370   371   372   373

α- and γ-Hydroxy cations (e.g. 372) are the conjugate acids of pyridones and pyrones (e.g. 373) and are considered in the next section.

The hetero ring does not usually influence hydroxyl groups separated from it by at least one saturated carbon atom. An exception is the ready dehydration (reverse of Michael addition) of α- or γ-(2-hydroxyethyl) groups (e.g. 374 → 375).

374   375   376   377   378

(*d*) *Pyridones, Pyrones, and Thiopyrones.* As discussed in the preceding section, these compounds are mesomeric with zwitterionic and carbonyl canonical forms (e.g. 376 ↔ 377, Z = NR, O, S). They are usually quite stable and highly aromatic in that they revert to type (see Section 1.3.*iii*). An overall treatment of their reactivity is given in Section 2.III.A.3. Electrophilic attack on the oxygen atom of the carbonyl group and nucleophilic attack on the carbon atom of the carbonyl group, in reactions which lead to substitution rather than to ring opening, are discussed in this section.

(*i*) Electrophilic attack on oxygen. Pyridones and pyrones are weak bases: 4- and 2-pyridone have pK_a values of 3·3 and 0·8, respectively. Proton addition occurs at the carbonyl oxygen atom (e.g. 376 ↔ 377 → 378). O-Alkylation of pyridones can be effected with diazomethane; 2-pyridone forms 2-methoxypyridine. Frequently O- and N-alkylation occur together: 4-pyridone with CH_2N_2 yields both 4-methoxypyridine and 1-methyl-4-pyridone. O-Acylation of pyridones may be effected with acid chlorides. Alkylation of pyridones *via* the anion is discussed in Section 2.III.F.1.

(*ii*) Nucleophilic displacements. Pyridones and pyrones behave as cyclic amides and esters and, predictably, do not normally react with nucleophilic 'ketonic reagents' such as HCN, RNH_2, $NaHSO_3$, NH_2OH, N_2H_4, PhN_2H_3, and $NH_2CON_2H_3$. Stronger nucleophilic reagents, i.e. those of the type that attack amides, generally also react with pyridones and pyrones. Thus, pyridones can be converted into chloropyridines with $POCl_3$ or PCl_5 [e.g. 2-methyl-4-quinolone (379) gives (380)]. Similarly, bromopyridines may be prepared using PBr_5. Alkyl substituents on the pyridone nitrogen atom are usually lost in reactions of this type. Phosphorus pentasulphide converts carbonyl groups into thiocarbonyl groups (e.g. 379 $\longrightarrow$ 381). Recently, reactions of γ-pyrones with active methylene groups have been reported [e.g. $CH_2(CN)_2$ reacts with 2,6-dimethyl-4-pyrone to give (382)].

379   380   381   382

7. Nitrogen-Containing Functional Groups

(*a*) *Amino-Imino Tautomerism.* 2- and 4-Aminopyridines (e.g. 383) can also exist in tautomeric pyridonimine forms (e.g. 385). However, basicity measurements (cf. Section **7.**4) show that the pyridonimine forms are unimportant, accounting for only about one part in 10^4. This behaviour is in direct contrast to that of the 2- and 4-hydroxy-pyridines which exist largely as pyridones (see Section **2.IV.A.6.***c*). This difference can be rationalized by consideration of the mesomerism of the alternative forms. Resonance stabilization of amino-pyridines (383 $\leftrightarrow$ 384) is greater than that of hydroxypyridines, while resonance stabilization of pyridonimines (385 $\leftrightarrow$ 386) is less than that of pyridones.

383   384   385   386

(*b*) α- *and* γ-*Amino Groups.* In 2- and 4-aminopyridines, canonical forms of type (384) increase the reactivity of the annular nitrogen atom and the α- and γ-carbon atoms (cf. Section **2.III.A.5**) towards electrophilic reagents, but decrease that of the amino group. Consequently, protons, alkylating agents, and metal ions react at the annular nitrogen atom (cf. Section **2.III.B.1**). Other electrophiles, i.e. those responsible for nitration, sulphonation, and halogenation, react at the ring carbon atoms (cf. Sections **2.III.C.1–3**).

However, some electrophilic reagents react at the amino group. Reactions of this type occur when the initial reaction at the pyridine nitrogen atom forms an unstable product which dissociates to regenerate the reactants or undergoes rearrangement inter- or intra-molecularly. These reactions are illustrated for 2-aminopyridine in formulae (387)–(398).

(*i*) Carboxylic and sulphonic acid chlorides and anhydrides give acylamino- (389) and sulphonamido-pyridines (390), respectively.

(*ii*) Nitric acid–sulphuric acid gives nitramino compounds (388) which are easily rearranged to C-nitro derivatives (387) (cf. Section 2.III.C.1).

(*iii*) Oxidation by persulphuric acid yields nitropyridines (397).

(*iv*) Nitrous acid gives highly unstable diazonium salts (394) which react with halide ions to yield products of type (395).

(*v*) Azacyanines are formed by reaction with quaternized halogeno compounds followed by quaternization (393 → 392 → 396).

The stability of pyridine-2- and -4-diazonium ions resembles that of aliphatic rather than benzenoid diazonium ions. Benzene diazonium ions are stabilized by mesomerism (399), which involves electron donation from the ring. Electron donation of this type is unfavourable in 2- and 4-substituted pyridines, hence the instability of pyridine-2- and -4-diazonium salts is not unexpected. On formation they react immediately with the aqueous solvent to form pyridones (391). However, if the diazotization is carried out in concentrated HCl or HBr, chloro- and bromo-pyridines (395) may be obtained in useful yields.

Just as canonical forms of type (384) decrease the susceptibility of 2- and 4-amino groups to electrophilic attack, they facilitate proton loss from the amino groups; the anions formed (e.g. 400 ↔ 401) react with electrophilic reagents preferentially at the amino nitrogen atom. 2-Aminopyridine (402) can be converted by $NaNH_2$–MeI into the 2-methylamino derivative (403) in this way.

399   400   401   402   403

(c) *β-Amino Groups*. The reactions of β-amino groups are very similar to those of the amino group in aniline. The diazonium salts are reasonably stable, undergo coupling and replacement reactions, and can be reduced to hydrazines.

(d) *Other Amino Groups*. α- and γ-Amino groups on pyridinium rings can lose a proton to form pyridonimines (e.g. 404 → 405) which are unstable and strongly basic (pK_a *ca.* 12).

α- and γ-Aminopyridine 1-oxides exist predominantly in the amino form, e.g. as (406) rather than as (407). Amino N-oxides can be diazotized, and the diazonium salts undergo coupling reactions, etc. These diazonium salts are stabilized by mesomerism (408) (cf. 399).

404   405   406   407   408

(e) *Nitro Groups*. α- and γ-Nitro groups on pyridines and pyridine 1-oxides are smoothly displaced by nucleophilic reagents, indeed, more readily than are α- and γ-halogen atoms. Thus, 4-nitropyridine

(409) is converted by sodium ethoxide at 80° into the 4-ethoxy derivative (410). Such reactions are of particular importance for N-oxides
where the nitro derivatives are readily available by direct nitration;
their importance is exemplified by the following transformations:
(412) → (411), and (412) → (413, X = Cl, Br). The reactions involving hydrogen bromide and chloride are acid catalyzed (cf. 414),
while those with acetyl chloride probably proceed *via* intermediates
of type (415). 4-Nitropyridine gives (416) and other products on
keeping (cf. the polymerization of 4-halogenopyridines, Section
2.IV.A.5).

409   410   411   412   413

414   415   416

   Nitro compounds are easily reduced, catalytically or chemically,
to amino compounds. Incomplete reduction can lead to a hydroxyl-
amino derivative or to binuclear azo, azoxy, and hydrazo compounds
(e.g. 418 → 417, 419). A nitro group can be selectively reduced in
the presence of an N-oxide group (e.g. 412 → 420).

417   418   419   420

8. Sulphur-Containing Functional Groups

(*a*) *Mercapto-Thione Tautomerism.* Pyridines with α- or γ-mercapto
groups exist predominantly in the pyridinethione form, i.e. as (422)
rather than in the mercapto form (421). This behaviour is analogous
to that of the corresponding hydroxypyridines (cf. Section **2.IV.A.6.**c).

(*b*) *Thiones.* Pyridinethiones behave as cyclic thioamides and show reactions typical of thioamides. Thus, they react with electrophiles at the sulphur atom:

(*i*) Alkyl halides give alkylthio derivatives (422 → 423).
(*ii*) Iodine oxidizes them to disulphides (422 → 424).
(*iii*) Strong oxidation forms a sulphonic acid (422 → 425).

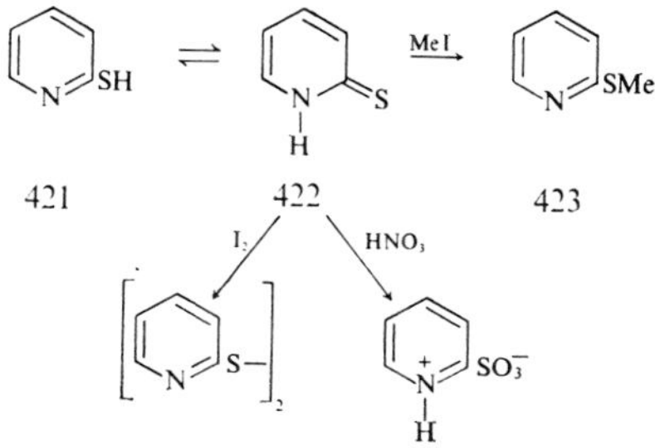

421   422   423

424   425

Pyridinethiones and pyranthiones also react as thioamides or thioesters with the typical nucleophilic 'ketonic' reagents; for example, thiocoumarin (426) with phenylhydrazine forms the hydrazone (427).

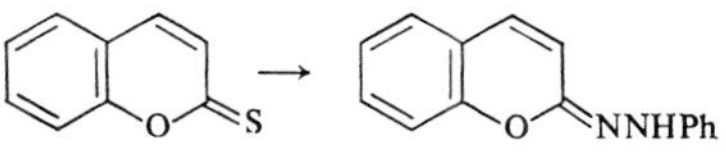

426   427

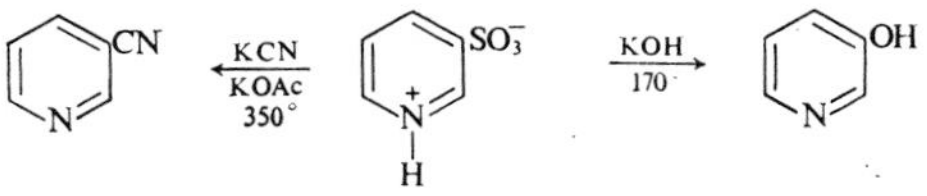

428   429   430

(*c*) *Sulphonic Acid Groups.* Pyridinesulphonic acids exist as zwitterions (e.g. 429). Apart from this, they behave very much as does phenylsulphonic acid, and the sulphonic acid group can be replaced by cyano or hydroxyl groups under vigorous conditions (e.g. 429 → 428, 430).

B. SUBSTITUENTS ON THE RING NITROGEN ATOM

The most important substituents are those in which an oxygen or carbon atom is directly attached to the pyridine nitrogen atom. The reactions of these N-substituted compounds show similarities, and their reactions are therefore discussed as types rather than treating the reactions of each substituent separately. The following reaction types are distinguished:

(*i*) N-Oxides and alkyl-pyridinium compounds undergo rearrangements (cf. 431 —→ 432).

(*ii*) Most substituents on nitrogen can be removed by nucleophilic attack (433); this is often the reverse of their formation (cf. Section **2.III.B.**).

(*iii*) Hydrogen atoms on the substituent atom adjacent to the annular nitrogen atom can be removed as protons (434 —→ 435); the relative ease of proton loss depends on the adjacent substituent atom and is in the order C < N < O.

(*iv*) Zwitterions resulting from reactions of the last type can react with electrophilic reagents (436 —→ 437) to give various products.

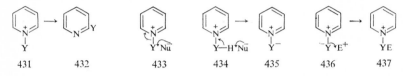

431   432   433   434   435   436   437

1. Rearrangement Reactions

1-Alkyl-pyridinium halides give mixtures of alkyl-pyridines on heating (e.g. 1-methylpyridinium iodide gives 2- and 4-picoline). This reaction is known as the Ladenburg rearrangement.

Pyridine 1-oxides heated with acid anhydrides are converted in good yield into pyridones (438 —→ 440), unless the N-oxide contains an α- or γ-alkyl group. In the latter case an alternative reaction occurs with acetic anhydride to form an α- or γ-acetoxyalkyl-pyridine (443). For attack on α- (441 —→ 443) and γ-alkyl groups, these reactions can be formulated in a manner similar to the *ortho*- and *para*-Claisen rearrangement, respectively, of allyl-phenol ethers. However, the formation of (443) has been claimed to proceed *via* a radical cage mechanism.

438   439   440

441   442   443

2. Loss of N-Substituents

Pyridine-halogen complexes (e.g. 444) dissociate on heating; halogen is lost so readily that these compounds act as mild halogenating agents towards, e.g., phenol or aniline. The complexes formed with boron trihalides (e.g. 445) and sulphur trioxide (446) are decomposed to pyridine by boiling water. Pyridine-sulphur trioxide is a mild sulphonating reagent (cf. the sulphonation of furan and pyrrole, Section **4.III.B.4**).

1-Acyl-pyridinium ions are very susceptible to attack by nucleophilic reagents and are good acylating agents (cf. Section **2.III.B.3.c**). 1-Alkyl-pyridinium halides dissociate reversibly into the alkyl halide and pyridine on vacuum distillation.

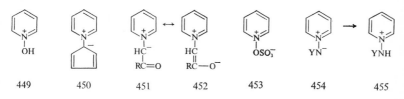

444   445   446   447   448

Reduction of N-oxides affords the parent heterocycles, and may be achieved by hydrogenation over palladium, by chemical reduction with Fe–HOAc, or by deoxygenation with phosphorus trichloride (cf. 447). 1-Alkoxy-pyridinium compounds react with hydroxide ions to give aldehydes plus pyridines (cf. 448).

3. Proton Loss from N-Substituents

1-Hydroxypyridinium ions (449) readily lose a proton to give pyridine 1-oxides; the N-oxides are themselves weak bases which form 1-hydroxypyridinium ions by proton addition. Proton loss from N-imides is more difficult, and ylid zwitterions can be isolated only in special cases (e.g. 450). The stability of ylids increases with increasing possibility for spreading the negative charge (cf. 451 ↔ 452).

449   450   451   452   453   454   455

4. Reactions of N-Substituents with Electrophilic Reagents

N-Oxides undergo the following reactions with electrophiles:

(*i*) Proton acids give 1-hydroxypyridinium salts (449).

(*ii*) Lewis acids form complexes [e.g. pyridine 1-oxide and SO$_3$ yield (453)].

(*iii*) Alkyl halides form 1-alkoxypyridinium salts (cf. 448).

N-Imides form salts with acids (454 $\longrightarrow$ 455) and can be acylated and sulphonylated. Thus, pyridine 1-imide with tosyl chloride gives (454, Y = Ts).

C. SUMMARY OF SYNTHETIC ROUTES TO SUBSTITUTED PYRIDINES

The preceding sections deal systematically with the reactions of substituents. A consequence of this treatment is that methods for the preparation of substituted compounds are scattered throughout the sections on the reactions of the aromatic rings and substituents.

Substituent group	Direct introduction of substituent (R)*	Obtainable indirectly by or starting from
Acyloxy	–	Hydroxyl compounds (**2.IV.A.6.***c*), N-oxides (**2.IV.B.1**)
Aldehyde	–	Oxidation (**2.IV.A.3**), halogeno compounds (**2.IV.A.5**)
Alkoxyl	–	Nitro (**2.IV.A.7.***e*), hydroxyl (**2.IV.A.6.***c*), and halogeno compounds (**2.IV.A.5**); pyrones (**2.IV.B.1**)
Alkyl	**2.III.D.5**; R	Pyridinium compounds (**2.IV.B.1**)
Alkylthio	–	Halogeno (**2.IV.A.5**) and thiocarbonyl compounds (**2.III.F.1**, **2.IV.A.8.***a*)
Amino	**2.III.D.2**; R	Halogeno (**2.IV.A.5**), amido (**2.IV.A.4**), and nitro compounds (**2.IV.A.7.***e*)
Aryl	**2.III.D.5**; R	–
Arylamino	–	Amines (**2.IV.A.7.***b*)
Azo	–	Nitro (**2.IV.A.7.***e*) and amino compounds (**2.IV.A.7.***a*)
Carboxylic acids, esters, etc.	R	Oxidation (**2.IV.A.2.***a*, *b*), halogeno compounds (**2.IV.A.5**)
Cyano	–	Pyridinium compounds (**2.III.D.5.***c*); carboxylic acids (**2.IV.A.4.***a*); sulphonic acids (**2.IV.A.8.***b*); halogeno (**2.IV.A.5**), vinyl (**2.IV.A.4.***c*), and Reissert compounds (**2.V.A.***b*)

Halogen	**2.III.C.3; 2.III.E.1; 2.IV.A.1.***d*	N-Oxides (**2.III.D.4**), nitro compounds (**2.IV.A.7.***e*), pyrones and pyridones (**2.IV.A.6.***d*), amines (**2.IV.A.7.***a*)
Hydrazino	–	Nitramines (**2.IV.A.7.***e*), halogeno (**2.IV.A.5**) and nitro compounds (**2.IV.A.7.***e*)
Hydroxyl, alcoholic	–	Alkyl (**2.IV.A.3**) and vinyl compounds (**2.IV.A.4.***c*), carboxylic acids (**2.IV.A.4.***a*)
Hydroxyl, phenolic	–	Halogeno compounds (**2.IV.A.5**), sulphonic acids (**2.IV.A.8.***b*)
Imino	–	Amines (**2.IV.A.7.***a*)
Keto	R	Alkyl compounds (**2.IV.A.3**), esters (**2.IV.A.4.***a*)
Mercapto	–	Halogeno compounds (**2.IV.A.5**)
Nitro	**2.III.C.1; 2.IV.A.2.***a*	Amines (**2.IV.A.7.***a*)
Nitroso	**2.III.C.4**	–
Sulphonic acid	**2.III.A.2; 2.IV.A.2.***a*	Halogeno (**2.IV.A.5**), thiocarbonyl (**2.IV.A.8**), and vinyl compounds (**2.IV.A.4.***c*)
Thiocarbonyl	–	Halogeno compounds (**2.IV.A.5.**), pyrones and pyridones (**2.IV.A.6.***d*)
Vinyl	–	Alkyl (**2.IV.A.3**) and hydroxyl compounds (**2.IV.A.6.***b*)

* R in this column signifies that compounds containing these substituents are commonly prepared by ring synthesis (see **2.II.A–D**).

Therefore, for convenient reference, the principal preparative methods for substituted compounds are tabulated here with cross-references.

The most frequently used methods for introducing substituents into the various positions of the pyridine nucleus are the following.

(*a*) *2-Position.* Substituents in the 2-position are often introduced *via* the Tschitschibabin reaction, which gives 2-aminopyridines (Section **2.III.D.2**). These can be converted into 2-halogeno-pyridines (Section **2.IV.A.5**) and 2-pyridones (Section **2.IV.A.6.***d*), which are versatile intermediates.

(*b*) *4-Position.* Substituents in the 4-position are most frequently introduced by further transformations of the readily available 4-nitropyridine 1-oxide (Section **2.IV.A.7.***e*).

(*c*) *3-Position*. Substituents in the 3-position are more difficult to introduce. Pyridines can be halogenated, nitrated, and sulphonated in the 3-position, but yields are poor unless an activating substituent (which can subsequently be removed) is present in the 2-position. The resulting 3-nitro- and 3-halogeno-pyridines can be converted into other compounds by the usual methods of benzenoid chemistry. 3-Aminopyridine can be obtained by Hofmann degradation or Curtius rearrangement of nicotinamide.

V. REACTIONS OF NON-AROMATIC COMPOUNDS

Dihydro compounds are treated separately from tetra- and hexa-hydro compounds because their chemistry is closely related to that of the aromatic compounds. Some dihydro compounds are in equi-librium with aromatic compounds [e.g. the pseudo-bases (456 $\rightleftharpoons$ 457)], and these are considered in Section 2.III.D.1, 'Reactions of Aromatic Nuclei'.

456   457   458

A. DIHYDRO COMPOUNDS

(*a*) *Tautomerism*. Non-N-substituted dihydropyridines can exist in at least five tautomeric forms (cf. Section 2.I.1). The forms in which there is no hydrogen on the ring nitrogen atom normally predominate; compare in aliphatic chemistry where imines are generally more stable than vinylamines. However, other forms can be stabilized by substitution; e.g., (458) exists as shown because of conjugation of the NH with the ester groups.

(*b*) *Aromatization*. 9,10-Dihydroacridines (e.g. 459) and 5,6-dihydro-phenanthridines (e.g. 460) are oxidized to the fully aromatic com-pounds on exposure to air or by other oxidizing agents such as chromic oxide. Dihydropyridines and 1,2-dihydro-quinolines and -isoquinolines are also very easily oxidized; N_2O_4–NO is often used to oxidize dihydropyridines. Syntheses which should afford the di-hydro compounds often proceed directly to the fully aromatic products (cf. Section 2.II.B.1).

Pyrans (cf. Section **2.II.B.1**) and thiopyrans are also easily aromatized [e.g., (461) reacts with S_2Cl_2 to give benzothiopyrylium ion]. 3,4-Dihydroisoquinolines (e.g. 462), 3,4-dihydrocoumarins (e.g. 463), and 2,3-dihydrochromones (e.g. 464) are aromatized by either oxidation or dehydrogenation with sulphur or selenium at 300° or with palladium at 200°.

459   460

461   462   463   464

(*c*) *Other Reactions.* Dihydro compounds show reactions which parallel those of their aliphatic analogues provided that the ready aromatization reactions just discussed do not interfere. Thus, 2,3-dihydrochromones (464) show ketonic reactions; 3,4-dihydrocoumarins (463) behave as lactones, and 5,6-dihydrophenanthridines (460) react like N-alkyl-anilines.

Reduction of dihydro compounds to the tetra- or hexa-hydro derivatives is usually possible. For example, dihydroisoquinolines of type (462) form the corresponding tetrahydroisoquinolines with H_2/Pd or with Na/Hg–EtOH.

B. TETRA- AND HEXA-HYDRO COMPOUNDS

(*a*) *Aromatization.* The tetra- and hexa-hydro heterocycles can often be aromatized, but this is more difficult than in the corresponding dihydro series. Thus, the conversion of piperidines into pyridines typically requires dehydrogenation with palladium at 250°.

(*b*) *Ring Fission.* Cleavage of the heterocyclic ring is usually accomplished using degradative procedures which are also applicable in the aliphatic series. For example, a nitrogen-containing ring is opened by the von Braun method (amide–PCl_5) (e.g. 465 → 466), by the von Braun cyanoammonium route (e.g. 467 → 468), or by Hofmann exhaustive methylation (e.g. 469 → 470).

465   466   467   468

469   470

(c) Other Reactions. These compounds usually show the typical reactions of their aliphatic analogues. 1,2,3,4-Tetrahydroquinoline (471, Z = NH) is an N-alkyl-aniline; chroman (471, Z = O) is an aryl-ether; and 3-piperidone (472) is an amino-ketone.

471   472   473   474

(d) Stereochemistry. Whereas the aromatic systems are planar, partially and fully reduced six-membered rings are non-planar. Piperidine and morpholine exist in chair forms which are analogous to that of cyclohexane. Di- and poly-substituted piperidines and tetrahydro-pyrans can exist in *cis-* and *trans-*forms, and the *trans-* (473) and *cis-*isomers (474) of decahydroisoquinoline resemble the corresponding forms of the decalins. The lone pair of electrons on nitrogen usually behaves as though it were somewhat 'smaller' than a hydrogen atom.

Steric effects can alter the reactivity of a heterocyclic compound as compared to that of its aliphatic analogue; for example, piperidine is less sterically hindered and more strongly nucleophilic than diethylamine.

CHAPTER THREE

Six-Membered Rings with Two or More Heteroatoms

I. NOMENCLATURE AND IMPORTANT COMPOUNDS

1. Diazines

(a) *Monocyclic Compounds.* The three isomeric diazines, together with their systems of numbering and trivial names, are shown in formulae (1)–(3).

1	2	3
pyridazine	pyrimidine	pyrazine

Pyridazines do not occur naturally. Maleic acid hydrazide (4) is used as a selective plant growth inhibitor. A few pyrazines are natural products (e.g. 5), and others are important synthetic drugs, e.g. sulphapyrazine (6).

4	5	6
	aspergillic acid (antibiotic)	sulphapyrazine (bacteriostat)

Pyrimidine natural products are important. The nucleic acids (7, Y = H, OH) are essential constituents of all cells and thus of all living matter. The nucleic acids contain pyrimidine and purine bases (denoted by 'heterocycle' in formula 7); ribonucleic acids (RNA) (7, Y = OH) contain D-ribose and uracil (8), deoxyribonucleic acids (DNA) (7, Y = H) contain 2-deoxy-D-ribose and thymine (9), and both types contain phosphate residues, cytosine (10), adenine (11), and guanine (12). Mild degradation of the nucleic acids yields nucleo-

7	8	9
nucleic acid	uracil	thymine

10	11	12
cytosine	adenine	guanine

sides, which are pyrimidine or purine glycosides [e.g. uridine (13), cytidine (14, Y = H)], and nucleotides, which are nucleoside monophosphates [e.g. cytidine 3'-phosphate (14, Y = PO_3H_2)].

Synthetic derivatives (e.g. 15) of barbituric acid (16) are used as hypnotics. Vitamin B_1 (17) contains a pyrimidine ring.

13	14
uridine	cytidine

15	16	17
veronal (hypnotic)	barbituric acid	vitamin B_1

(b) *Benzo-Diazines*. The trivial names and numbering systems for the benzo-diazines are shown in formulae (18)–(23). The phenazine dyes used for silk and wool include aposafranine (24). A few phenazines are natural products, e.g. the antibiotic iodinin (25).

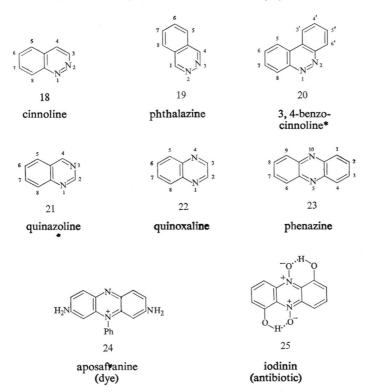

18
cinnoline

19
phthalazine

20
3, 4-benzo-
cinnoline*

21
quinazoline

22
quinoxaline

23
phenazine

24
aposafranine
(dye)

25
iodinin
(antibiotic)

(c) *Other Fused Diazines*. These include purine (26), pteridine (27), and alloxazine (28). Xanthopterin (2-amino-4,6-dihydroxypteridine) exemplifies the pterins,† which were first isolated from butterfly wings.

26
purine

27
pteridine

28
alloxazine

---

* Chemical Abstracts uses the name benzo[c]cinnoline and different numbering.
† These compounds probably exist in a tautomeric form (cf. 3.IV.4.a).

Some pteridines have recently been reported to have cofactor activity, e.g. in enzymic hydroxylations. The growth factor folic acid has structure (29). Riboflavin (30), a B vitamin, is a derivative of iso-alloxazine.

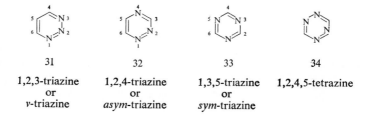

29

folic acid
(growth factor)

30

riboflavin
(B vitamin)

2. Other Compounds

(*a*) *Triazines and Tetrazines*. The names and systems of numbering for the triazines are given in diagrams (31)–(33). 1,2,4,5-Tetrazines (34) are known.

31	32	33	34
1,2,3-triazine	1,2,4-triazine	1,3,5-triazine	1,2,4,5-tetrazine
or	or	or	
v-triazine	*asym*-triazine	*sym*-triazine	

(*b*) *Oxazines and Thiazines*. 1,2-, 1,3-, and 1,4-Oxazines and -thiazines are the O- and S-analogues of the three isomeric diazines (1–3). These rings can accommodate only two double bonds, and there is one 'extra' hydrogen atom, the position of which must be indicated; e.g., three 1,3-oxazines could theoretically exist (35–37). Tetrahydro-1,4-oxazine (38), called morpholine, is widely used as a basic solvent and as a secondary amine.

35	36	37	38
2*H*-	4*H*-	6*H*-	morpholine

1,3-oxazine

39

phenoxazine

40

phenothiazine

41

42

Two of the benzo derivatives have commonly used trivial names, (39) and (40). Phenothiazine (40) has important insecticidal and anthelmintic applications. Several substituted phenoxazonium and phenothiazonium salts (cf. 41, Z = O, S) are used as dyes, e.g. methylene blue (42) which is a biological stain, oxidation-reduction indicator, and cotton dye.

II. RING SYNTHESES

Ring syntheses are subdivided according to the number and relative orientation of the heteroatoms in the ring formed. An account of syntheses of rings with heteroatoms in the 1,2- (43), 1,3- (44), and 1,4-positions (45) is followed by a survey of those for rings with more than two heteroatoms.

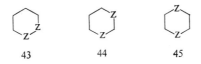

43   **44**   **45**

A. HETEROATOMS IN THE 1,2-POSITIONS

1. General Survey

The most important synthetic methods involve condensation of hydrazine, hydroxylamine, or hydrogen peroxide with a 1,4-dioxygenated carbon chain, and they are particularly useful for the preparation of pyridazines, phthalazines, oxazines and benzoxazines. However, cyclization of diazonium ions is most important in the cinnoline series. Other methods include Diels-Alder reactions of a diene with an azo or nitroso compound.

2. Methods Using Hydrazine or Hydroxylamine

1,4-Dicarbonyl compounds with a double bond in the 2,3-position condense with hydrazine to give pyridazines (e.g. 46 → 47). If one of the carbonyl groups in the starting material is part of a carboxyl group or a potential carboxyl group, then reactions with hydrazine or hydroxylamine lead to pyridazones or 1,2-oxazones (e.g. 48 → 49, Z = NH, NPh, O).

46   47   48   49

If the double bond is contained in a benzene ring, analogous reactions can occur; phthalaldehyde reacts with hydrazine to give phthalazine itself.

3. Other Methods

Reduced pyridazines, 1,2-oxazines, and 1,2-thiazines can be prepared by Diels-Alder-type reactions. Butadiene condenses with $(:NCO_2Et)_2$ and nitrosobenzene to yield (50) and (51), respectively.

50   51   52   53

54   55   56   57

o-Ethylenic, *o*-acetylenic, and *o*-diazonium ions cyclize spontaneously to give cinnolines or cinnolones (52 → 53; 54, 56 → 55). A somewhat analogous cyclization is involved in the preparation of the benzocinnoline (57) by irradiation of azobenzene.

B. HETEROATOMS IN THE 1,3-POSITIONS

1. General Survey

No important synthesis involves C–C bond formation, but all of the remaining possibilities (58–61) have been used. For the preparation

of pyrimidines, methods of type (58) are the most important. Quinazolines are prepared by routes of type (59), whereas saturated compounds, i.e. 1,3-dioxanes, 1,3-thioxanes, 1,3-dithianes, result from
syntheses of type (60).

58   59   60   61

2. Type C–C–C + Z–C–Z

A very large number of pyrimidines have been synthesized by reaction
of a 1,3-dicarbonyl compound, or a potential 1,3-dicarbonyl compound, with an amidine derivative; representative substituents are
shown in structures (62) and (63). The following modifications are
noteworthy:

(*i*) The amidine can be replaced by urea when 2-pyrimidones (64)
result.

(*ii*) If one or both of the carbonyl groups in the 1,3-dicarbonyl
compound is in the form of an ester, 4-pyrimidones (65) and their
6-hydroxy derivatives (66) result.

(*iii*) Replacement of one of the carbonyl groups by a cyano group
leads to 4-amino compounds (67).

(*iv*) If the central carbon atom of the carbonyl compound is tetra-
substituted, non-aromatic derivatives are produced [e.g. $Et_2C(CO_2Et)_2$
reacts with urea to yield veronal (68)].

62   63

R, R' = H, Me, Ph, CO_2Et
Y = H, Me, Ph, Br, NO, NO_2
Y' = H, Me, Ph, OMe, SMe, NH_2
Basic catalyst, e.g. NaOEt–EtOH

64   65   66   67   68

3. Type C–C–C–Z + C–Z

Quinazolines can be prepared by the reaction of *o*-acylanilines with
amides (69 → 70). Heating anthranilic acid (71) with amides or
amidines yields 4-quinazolinones (72).

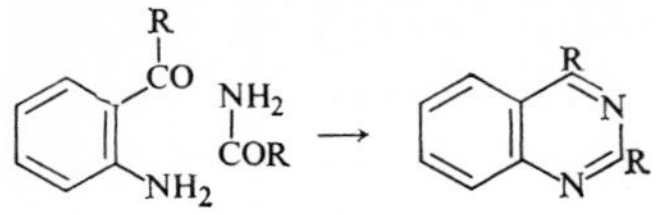

69   70 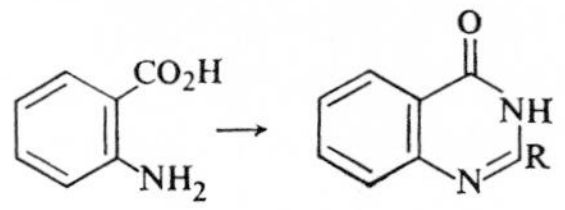   71   72

4. Type Z–C–C–C–Z + C

This route is used principally for the preparation of reduced pyrimidines, oxazines, thiazines, dioxanes, dithianes, and oxathianes (e.g. 74 → 73, 75; Z, Z′ = NH, O, S). The corresponding benzo derivatives are prepared similarly (e.g. from 76).

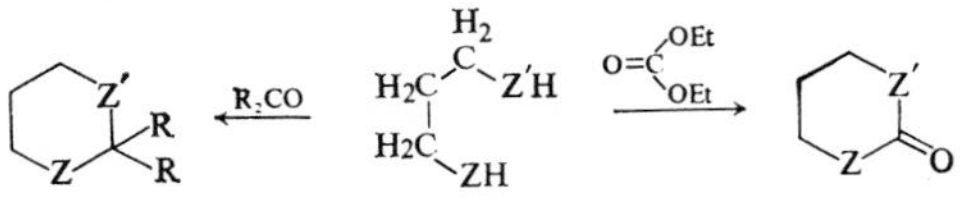

73   74   75

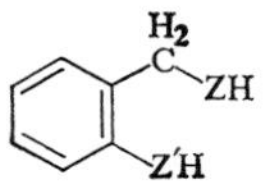

76

C. HETEROATOMS IN THE 1,4-POSITIONS

1. General Survey

The important synthetic methods can be divided into three types which are illustrated by structures (77)–(79).

(*i*) Quinoxalines, pteridines, phenazines, and phenoxazines are obtained by methods of type (77).

(*ii*) Pyrazines are prepared by scheme (78).

(*iii*) Reduced monocyclic rings, e.g. piperazines, dioxanes, and dithianes, are also synthesized by reactions of type (78).

(*iv*) Phenothiazines are obtained by route (79).

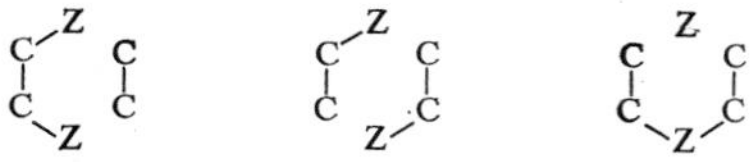

77   78   79

2. Type Z–C–C–Z + C–C

Syntheses of this type are important for the preparation of bi- and tri-cyclic compounds.

(*i*) *o*-Phenylenediamine reacts with α-diketones to give quinoxalines (80 → 81), and with *o*-quinones to give phenazines.

(*ii*) Heterocyclic *o*-diamines react analogously, as in, e.g., the preparation of pteridines (82 + 83 → 84).

(*iii*) *o*-Aminophenols react with quinones to give phenoxazonium salts (e.g. 85 + 86 → 87).

3. Type C–C–Z + C–C–Z

(*i*) An important preparation of pyrazines is from α-amino-ketones (88) which undergo spontaneous intermolecular cyclization to dihydropyrazines (89). The α-amino-ketones are often prepared *in situ* by reduction of isonitroso-ketones, and the dihydropyrazines are usually oxidized to pyrazines before isolation (cf. Section 3.V.2).

(*ii*) Piperazines, dioxanes, and dithianes can be prepared as shown (90, 92, → 91; Z = NH, O, S).

4. Type C–C–Z–C–C + Z

Phenothiazine, thianthrene, and phenoxathiin (94, Z = NH, S, O) are formed as illustrated (93 → 94).

93   94

D. COMPOUNDS WITH THREE OR FOUR HETEROATOMS

(*i*) Benzo-1,2,3-triazines are prepared by methods of the type illustrated by (95 → 96), which resemble those used for the synthesis of cinnolines (cf. Section 3.II.A.3).

95   96   97   98·

(*ii*) 1,2,4-Triazines can be prepared from amino-guanidines and α-dicarbonyl compounds (97 → 98).

(*iii*) 1,3,5-Triazines (99, Y = Cl, NH_2, Ph) are formed by the trimerization of the corresponding monomer, Y—C≡N, spontaneously or in the presence of catalysts. The analogous saturated heterocyclic systems are synthesized by trimerization, usually *in situ*, of compounds containing a C–Z bond [e.g. CH_3CHO → paraldehyde (100)].

99   100   101   102

(*iv*) 1,2,4,5-Tetrazines can be prepared as illustrated (101 → 102).

III. REACTIONS OF THE AROMATIC RINGS

1. General Survey

In so far as is possible, the following treatment parallels that adopted for the six-membered aromatic ring systems with one heteroatom (cf. Section 2.III). It should be noted, however, that some of the classes of compounds with two heteroatoms do not exist, and the reactions of others are not well investigated. Hence, most of the examples are taken from azine chemistry.

Extrapolating from benzene through pyridine to the diazines indicates the main trends of diazine chemistry. Reactions with electrophilic reagents are more difficult with diazines than with pyridine, both on the annular nitrogen atoms (weakened basicity) and on the ring carbon atoms (no reaction without activation). Conversely, nucleophilic attack is easier on a diazine than on pyridine, and reagents which react only with quaternized pyridine derivatives will sometimes react with the parent diazines.

The diazines show aromatic behaviour and have resonance energies which are considerable, but probably less than those of benzene or pyridine (exact values are uncertain because of experimental difficulties in their combustion). In most of their reactions diazines tend to revert to type. Phenoxazonium and phenothiazonium salts, oxazones, and thiazones are evidently less stabilized by resonance for they show far less tendency to revert to type.

2. Electrophilic Attack on the Ring Nitrogen Atoms

The basicity of the diazines is sharply reduced from that of pyridine (pK_a 5·2): the pK_a of pyrazine is 0·4, pyrimidine 1·1, and pyridazine 2·1. A fused benzene ring has little effect on the pK_a values in the cases of quinoxaline (*ca.* 0·6) and cinnoline (2·6). Quinazoline, however, has a pK_a of 3·3 and is a much stronger base than pyrimidine, but this is due to the fact that the quinazolinium cation is covalently hydrated (see Section **3.III.4**).

Alkyl halides react with diazines less readily than with pyridines. If the nitrogen atoms are α or β to each other (e.g. pyridazines, pyrimidines), only mono-quaternary salts are formed. Cinnoline undergoes quaternization at the 2-position. Quinoxalines and phenazines yield di-quaternary salts under forcing conditions ($Et_3O^+ BF_4^-$ as reagent).

The formation of N-oxides by peracid oxidation is analogous to the preparation of the quaternary salts. The N-oxides are formed less readily than in the pyridine series, and only pyrazine and its benzo derivatives are easily converted into di-N-oxides, although cinnoline di-N-oxides have recently been reported.

3. Electrophilic Attack on the Ring Carbon Atoms

Unactivated diazines do not undergo substitution reactions involving attack by electrophilic reagents on the carbon atoms. Diazines with one strongly activating group (e.g. OR, NH_2) are substituted with difficulty, approximately as readily as pyridine. Diazines with two such groups are substituted easily ($\approx$ benzene), and diazines with three such groups very readily ($\approx$ phenol). A diazinone behaves as a singly activated diazine.

Pyrimidines normally undergo electrophilic substitution at the 5-position. When activating groups are present in each of the 2-, 4-, and 6-positions, nitrosation, Mannich reactions, and diazo-coupling proceed readily. Halogenation can also be effected when one or two activating groups are present (Br_2 or Cl_2 in H_2O, AcOH, or $CHCl_3$, 20–100°).

4. Nucleophilic Attack on the Ring Carbon Atoms

With hydroxide ions diazine-onium salts form pseudo-bases which readily undergo ring fission; e.g. 3-methylquinazolinium ion yields (103).

103   104

In acid solution, quinazoline is 'covalently hydrated' to form the cation (104). Such covalent hydration is probably a widespread phenomenon.

Amide ions react with diazines. Sodamide converts 4-methyl-pyrimidine successively into the 2-mono- and 2,6-di-amino derivatives, and pyrazine gives 2-aminopyrazine.

Organometallic reagents give the expected products; e.g. 2,5-dimethylpyrazine with lithium aryls affords the 3-aryl derivatives.

105   106   107   108

Diazines are readily reduced catalytically and chemically. The ring can be cleaved when the two nitrogens are adjacent: thus pyridazine gives tetramethylenediamine as well as partially hydrogenated products on reduction with sodium and ethanol. Cinnolines form either dihydro derivatives (e.g. 106 → 105) or indoles by ring opening and reclosure (e.g. 106 → 107). Phthalazine gives 1,2,3,4-tetrahydro-phthalazine (with Na/Hg) or the ring-opened product (108) (with Zn–HCl). Pyrazines and pyrimidines are normally reduced to hexahydro derivatives, whereas quinazolines are quinoxalines usually give 1,2,3,4-tetrahydro derivatives (e.g. with Na–EtOH).

IV. REACTIONS OF SUBSTITUENTS ON AROMATIC RINGS

Since oxazonium and thiazonium salts are not well known except in the dibenzo series, and since oxazones, thiazones, triazones, triazines, and tetrazines are relatively unimportant and little investigated, this section deals largely with substituents on diazines and their benzo derivatives.

1. General Survey

Substituents α or γ to a ring nitrogen atom behave similarly to 2- and 4-substituents on pyridine (cf. Section 2.IV.A). The effect of the second nitrogen atom in diazines is to push the reactivity further in the direction of the corresponding carbonyl compound (cf. discussion in Section 2.IV.A.1). An example of this is that nucleophilic displacement of a cyano group, as in (109 → 110), does not normally occur in the pyridine series, rather it is analogous to the reactions of aliphatic acyl cyanides (RCO–CN).

109   110

111   112   113

Substituents in the 5-position of pyrimidines (111) are the only substituents on azines which are not α or γ to a ring nitrogen atom, and these behave similarly to the substituents in the 3-position of pyridines. Bond fixation causes 3-substituents in cinnolines (112) to react like 3-substituents in isoquinolines.

In benzopyridines, electrophilic reagents attack the annular nitrogen atom and the benzene ring(s), whereas nucleophilic reagents attack the heterocyclic ring at the α- or γ-carbon atoms. These generalizations hold in benzo-diazine chemistry (see Sections **3.III.3** and **IV.2**). However, in phenazonium, phenoxazonium, and phenothiazonium ions (113, Z = NR, O, S), nucleophilic reagents cannot readily attack the heterocyclic ring, and reaction occurs at the 3-position (113) because the electron deficiency is sufficiently great to allow attack on the fused benzene ring. Reactions of this type are discussed in Section **3.IV.2**.

2. Carbon-Containing Substituents

(a) *Fused Benzene Rings.* Electrophilic substitution normally occurs in the benzo ring of benzo-diazines. The orientation for the nitration of cinnoline and quinazoline is shown in diagrams (114) and (115). Strong oxidation (e.g. $KMnO_4$–OH^-) degrades fused benzene rings to carboxylic acid residues; e.g. phthalazine gives (116) and phenazine yields successively (117) and (118).

114	115	116

117	118

As discussed in Section **3.IV.1**, nucleophilic reagents can attack the benzene rings in phenazonium, phenoxazonium, and phenothiazonium ions (119, Z = NR, O, S). Hydroxide ions give pseudo-base intermediates (120) which are oxidized (by air, Br_2, etc.) to the pyridone analogues (121) before isolation. Ammonia and amines (e.g. $PhNH_2$, Me_2NH) give initial adducts of type (122), which are then oxidized (with air, Br_2, etc.) to new onium salts (123).

119	120	121

122	123

(*b*) *Aryl Groups.* Phenyl groups attached to the carbon atoms of diazines undergo electrophilic substitution reactions predominantly at the *meta* positions as shown for the nitration of the pyrazine derivative (124).

124

(*c*) *Alkyl Groups.* Alkyl groups are 'active' when they are α or γ to a nitrogen atom, as in 3-methylpyridazine, 1-methylphthalazine, and 2-methylpyrazine. Such alkyl groups react with aldehydes, halogens, potassium permanganate, etc., much as does the methyl group in 2-picoline (see Section **2.IV.A.3.***a*). Alkylation and acylation of methyl groups can also be carried out (cf. Section **2.IV.A.3.***b*).

The reactivity of alkyl groups α or γ to two nitrogen atoms, like those in 2- or 4-methylpyrimidine, is further enhanced; for example, Claisen condensation with ethyl oxalate is possible. In quinazolines partial double bond fixation makes a methyl group in the 4-position more reactive than one in the 2-position. α or γ-Methyl groups in onium salts show the expected high reactivity (cf. Section **2.IV.A.3.***d*).

(*d*) *Carboxylic Acids, Aldehydes, and Ketones.* Compounds containing these groups show reactions similar to those of the benzene and pyridine analogues. Carboxyl groups α or γ to a ring nitrogen atom are readily lost on heating; thus, 2-pyrazinecarboxylic acid gives pyrazine at 200°, and 4,5-pyrimidinedicarboxylic acid forms the 5-mono-acid on vacuum distillation.

3. Halogen Atoms

As expected, halogens are 'active' when they are α or γ to a ring nitrogen atom. 3-Chloropyridazine (125) and 2-chloropyrazine, for example, undergo the usual nucleophilic replacements (cf. Section **2.IV.A.5**) rather more readily than does 2-chloropyridine.

In polyhalogeno compounds such as 2,4,6-trichloropyrimidine,

125   126   127

each successive chlorine atom is replaced more slowly than the last because the groups introduced (e.g. NH_2) partially cancel the activating effect of the annular nitrogen atoms. A halogen atom in the 4-position is more reactive than one in the 2-position of quinazoline because of partial double bond fixation. Thus, in 2,4-dichloroquinazoline (126), replacement occurs almost exclusively in the 4-position, whereas 2,4-dichloropyrimidine (127) yields approximately equal amounts of the 2- and 4-mono-replacement products.

| 128 | 129 | 130 |

4. Oxygen-Containing Functional Groups

(a) *Tautomerism.* Physical methods show that compounds with a potential hydroxyl group α or γ to a ring nitrogen atom exist largely in the carbonyl form. Where alternative carbonyl forms are possible, that with the carbonyl α to the NH group is somewhat more stable, thus *ca.* 2 parts of (128) exist in equilibrium with one part of (129).

A rare exception to the above generalization is maleic hydrazide, where one of the two potential α-hydroxyl groups does occur as such (130).

Hydroxyl groups in the 5-position of pyrimidines exist as such, as would be expected.

(b) *Diazinones.* The diazinones react similarly to pyridones (Section 2.IV.A.6.d). They can be converted into chloro-diazines by $POCl_3$

| 131 | 132 |

| 133 | 134 | 135 |

136   137

[e.g. uric acid (131) yields 2,6,8-trichloropurine (132)]. Alkylation can give either O- or N-alkyl products or a mixture of both; phthalazinone (134) gives the O-methyl derivative (133) with Me_2SO_4–$PhNO_2$, but methylation under basic conditions (MeI–KOH) forms the N-methyl compound (135).

(*c*) *Alkoxyl Groups.* α- and γ-Alkoxyl groups undergo nucleophilic replacement. This reaction is facilitated in the pyrimidine series because the alkoxyl groups are α and γ to *two* nitrogen atoms; it is often used to prepare amino-pyrimidines. α- or γ-Alkoxyl compounds rearrange easily to N-substituted diazinones (e.g. 136 → 137).

5. Nitrogen- and Sulphur-Containing Functional Groups
(*a*) *Amino Groups.* Amino compounds have been shown to exist largely as such, and not as the tautomeric imino compounds, by physical methods (cf. Sections **7.3–6**). Amino groups in 5-amino-pyrimidines (i.e. β-amino groups) behave like that in aniline, but compounds with α- or γ-amino groups resemble their pyridine analogues. Thus, α- or γ-amino groups are difficult to diazotize, are readily hydrolyzed (e.g. H_2SO_4–H_2O at 100°) to the corresponding diazinone, and give unstable acyl compounds (easily hydrolyzed back to the amine).

(*b*) *Nitro and Nitroso Groups* on diazines generally react similarly to those attached to pyridine rings (cf. Section **2.IV.A.7.**e).

(*c*) *Sulphur-Containing Groups.* Compounds with potential mercapto groups α or γ to a ring nitrogen atom exist largely in the thione form (cf. Section **2.IV.A.8.**a).

138

Pyrimidinethiones (e.g. 138) are well known as intermediates and can be converted into the following classes of compounds:

(*i*) Chloropyrimidines, by PCl_5.

(*ii*) Alkylthiopyrimidines, by alkyl iodides.

(*iii*) Pyrimidinones, by hydrolysis with $HCl-H_2O$.

(*iv*) Pyrimidine disulphides, by I_2.

(*v*) The sulphur-free pyrimidine, by oxidation with H_2O_2 or HNO_3; this reaction probably proceeds *via* the sulphinic acid.

V. REACTIONS OF NON-AROMATIC COMPOUNDS

In general, the non-aromatic compounds are fairly readily aromatized. Apart from this, they tend to behave very much as their aliphatic analogues.

1. Reactions Involving 'Reversion to Type'

One surprising feature of some 1,4-dithiin derivatives is that although they possess non-planar rings (cf. 139) and electron octets rather than sextets, they do show some tendency to 'revert to type'. Nitration of 2,5-diphenyl-1,4-dithiin (140) and nitration (HNO_3–AcOH) and acetylation (H_3PO_4–Ac_2O) of benzo-1,4-dithiin (141) occur in the hetero rings as indicated.

139   140   141   142

143   144   145   146

2. Aromatization

Dihydro-diazines are readily aromatized by oxidizing agents: 4,5-dihydropyridazine (142) yields pyridazine (CrO_3–AcOH), and 3,4-dihydroquinazoline (143) is converted by $K_3Fe(CN)_6$ into quinazoline. Phenoxazines and phenothiazines (cf. 144, Z = O, S) may be oxidized to phenoxazonium and phenothiazonium salts (145, Z = O, S).

Some dihydro-diazines disproportionate: the dihydrocinnoline (146) on treatment with hydrochloric acid gives 4-phenylcinnoline and 4-phenyl-1,2,3,4-tetrahydrocinnoline.

3. Other Reactions

In general, the non-aromatic compounds undergo the reactions which are typical of their aliphatic analogues. Thus 1,3-dioxane behaves as an acetal, 1,4-dioxane as a bis-ether, and 2,5-dioxopiperazine (147) as a bis-lactam.

Piperazine (148, Z = NH) and morpholine (148, Z = O) show typical aliphatic secondary amine properties, but their pK_a values,

147 148

9·8 and 8·4, respectively (cf. piperidine pK_a 11·2), reflect the inductive effect of the second heteroatom.

CHAPTER FOUR

Five-Membered Rings with One Heteroatom

I. NOMENCLATURE AND IMPORTANT COMPOUNDS

1. Aromatic Monocyclic Compounds

(*a*) *Nomenclature*. The parent ring systems with two double bonds are called thiophene (1), pyrrole (2), and furan (3). Nuclear positions are designated with arabic numerals (cf. 1), or, less frequently, with Greek letters (cf. 2).

1	2	3
thiophene	pyrrole	furan

4	5	6
mesobilirubin (bile pigment)	α-	β-
	pyrrolenine	

The radicals derived from these rings are named thienyl, pyrrolyl, and furyl. The 2-furylmethyl radical is called furfuryl. Compounds in which two pyrrole nuclei are joined by a CH_2 group are called 'dipyrromethanes'; when the linkage is by a CH group, as in (4), they are named 'dipyrromethenes'.

Derivatives of the unstable tautomeric forms (5) and (6) of pyrrole are known.

(*b*) *Thiophenes*. Thiophene and its homologues occur in coal-tar benzene, shale oil, and crude petroleum. They show the indophenine test (Section **4.III.B.7.**b), and the discovery of thiophene followed the observation that pure benzene did not give this test. Thiophenes are sometimes named after the benzenoid analogues, e.g. thiotolene for methylthiophene, thiotenol for hydroxythiophene.

(*c*) *Furans*. Furfural (7) arises from the decomposition of sugars (Section **4.II.2.**c) and is a commercially important raw material used in furfural-phenol resins and as a synthetic intermediate (see Section **4.III.C.2**).

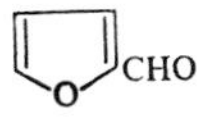

7

furfural

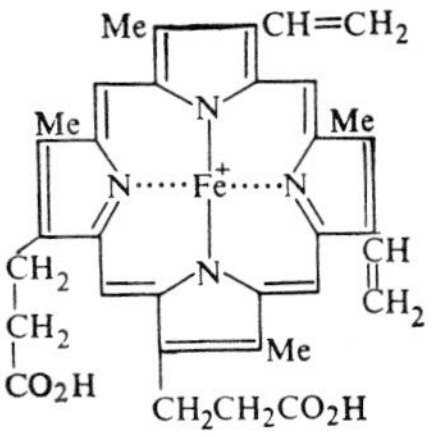

8

haemin
(blood pigment)

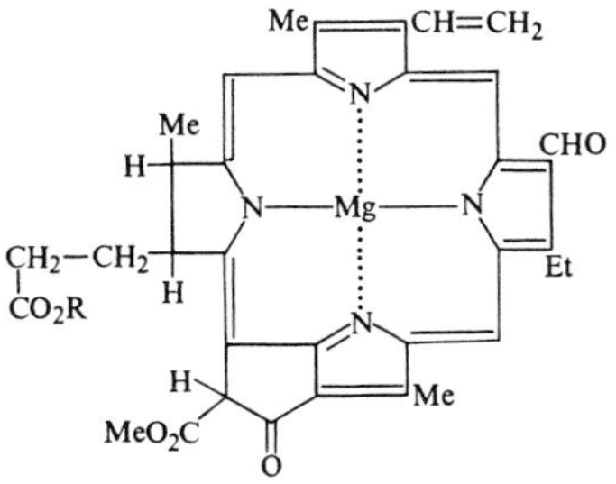

9

chlorophyll-b
(R = phytyl, $C_{20}H_{34}$)

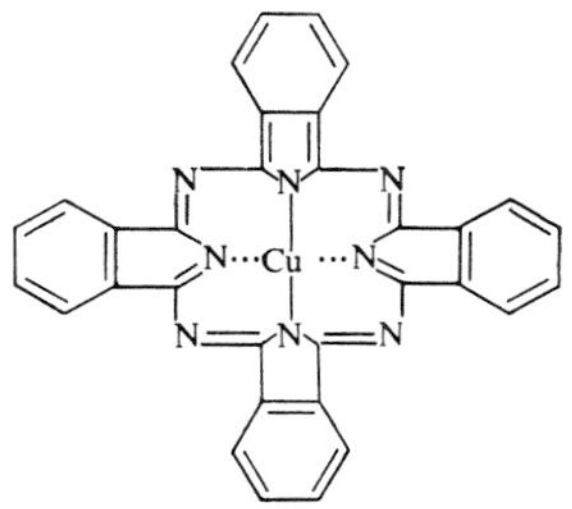

10

monastral blue
(phthalocyanine pigment)

(*d*) *Pyrroles*. Pyrrole occurs in bone oil and imparts a bright red colour to pine wood moistened with mineral acid; this characteristic behaviour led to its discovery and is used as a qualitative test for pyrrole derivatives.

The bile pigments, e.g. mesobilirubin (4), are metabolic products having chains of four pyrrole rings. Their precursors are the porphyrins, which comprise the blood pigments (e.g. 8), the chlorophylls (e.g. 9), and vitamin B_{12}, and consist of four pyrrole units joined in a macro ring.

The phthalocyanines (e.g. 10) are important synthetic pigments.

2. Non-Aromatic Monocyclic Compounds

(*a*) *Nomenclature.* Reduced thiophenes and furans are named systematically as 2,3-dihydro (11), 2,5-dihydro (12), and 2,3,4,5-tetrahydro compounds (13). Alternatively, *delta* (Δ) can be used to indicate the position of the remaining double bond, thus (11) and (12) are named as Δ^2- and Δ^3-dihydro compounds, respectively; tetrahydrothiophene is also called thiophane.

Reduced pyrroles have trivial names; the dihydro derivatives, of which there are three types, are designated as Δ^1- (14), Δ^2-, and Δ^3-pyrrolines, and the tetrahydropyrroles are called pyrrolidines.

11   12   13   14

(*b*) *Reduced Furans.* Reduced furan rings occur in many important anhydrides, lactones, hemi-acetals, and ethers. Maleic anhydride (15) is frequently used as a dienophile in Diels–Alder reactions, and it is a component of alkyd resins. Several unsaturated γ-lactones are natural products (e.g. 16–18), while the furanose sugars (e.g. 19) are cyclic hemi-acetals.

15   16   17   18

maleic   ascorbic acid or α- ———————— β-
anhydride   vitamin C   angelica lactone

19

β-D-fructofuranose
or fructose

c) *Reduced Pyrroles.* The imides, lactams, and imines related to the oxygen-containing compounds mentioned in the preceding section are also important. The amino-acids proline (20, Y = H) and hydroxyproline (20, Y = OH) occur in proteins, and N-bromo-succinimide (21) is widely used to effect free radical bromination.

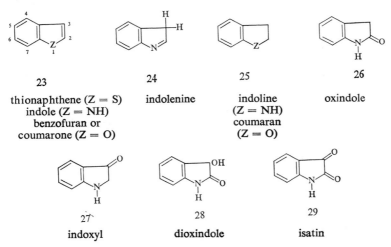

20	21	22
		biotin or
		vitamin H

(*d*) *Reduced Thiophenes*. Biotin (22), an H-vitamin which occurs in egg yolk, is the most important of the reduced thiophenes.

3. 2,3-Benzo Derivatives

(*a*) *Nomenclature*. The fully aromatic compounds are named and numbered as shown in diagram (23). Derivatives of the isomeric form (24) of indole are named as indolenines.

The common names indoline (25, Z = NH) and coumaran (25, Z = O) are used for the 2,3-dihydro derivatives of indole and benzofuran, respectively. The oxo-indolines are named as indicated in formulae (26)–(29) (see Section **4.V.1.***b* for a discussion of the tautomerism of these oxo compounds).

23	24	25	26
thionaphthene (Z = S)	indolenine	indoline	oxindole
indole (Z = NH)		(Z = NH)	
benzofuran or		coumaran	
coumarone (Z = O)		(Z = O)	

27	28	29
indoxyl	dioxindole	isatin

(*b*) *Indoles*. There are many important indole derivatives.

   (*i*) Indigo (30), a vat dye known and widely used since antiquity, was obtained from indican (31), a β-glucoside of indoxyl which occurs in some plants; indigo is now prepared synthetically. Tyrian purple, a natural dye used since classical times, is 6,6′-dibromoindigo (cf. 30).

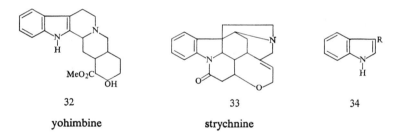

30	31
indigo	indican

(*ii*) The numerous indole alkaloids include complex derivatives such as yohimbine (32) and strychnine (33).

(*iii*) Tryptophan [34, R = CH₂CH(NH₂)CO₂H] is an essential amino-acid found in most proteins; its metabolites include skatole (34, R = Me) and tryptamine (34, R = CH₂CH₂NH₂).

(*iv*) 3-Indoleacetic acid (34, R = CH₂CO₂H) is important as a plant growth hormone.

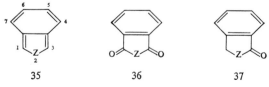

32	33	34
yohimbine	strychnine	

4. Other Compounds

(*a*) *3,4-Benzo Derivatives.* The fully unsaturated compounds are named and numbered as shown in diagram (35); derivatives of all these are known but are rather unstable (see Section **4.III.A.*b***).

35	36	37

isothionaphthene (Z = S)
isoindole (Z = NH)
isobenzofuran (Z = O)

Partially saturated compounds are usually named as derivatives of phthalic acid. Phthalic anhydride and phthalimide (36, Z = O, NH) are important commercial intermediates for the preparation of dyes and are used in plastics, etc. The lactone and lactam (37, Z = O, NH) are called phthalide and phthalimidine, respectively.

(*b*) *Dibenzo Derivatives.* The fully aromatic compounds are named dibenzothiophene, carbazole, and dibenzofuran (38, Z = S, NH, O); the system of numbering shown in (38) has been adopted for this book. Since 1936, *Chemical Abstracts* has used the system of numbering shown in (39) for dibenzofurans and dibenzothiophenes but retained that shown in (38) for carbazoles. Prior to 1936, one system (38) was used in all cases.

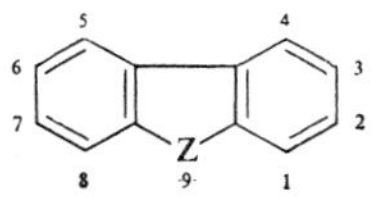

38 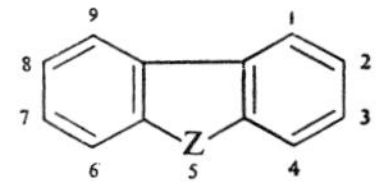   39

dibenzothiophene (Z = S)
carbazole (Z = NH)
dibenzofuran (Z = O)

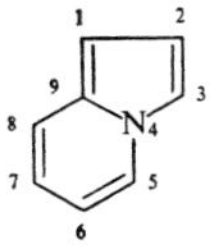

40   41

indolizine   β-carboline
or
pyrrocoline

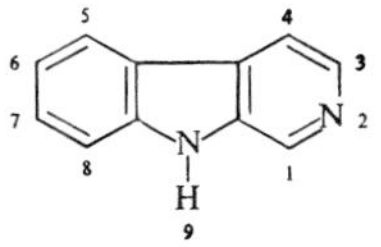

(*c*) *Other Fused Ring Compounds.* Indolizine (40) is a derivative of both pyrrole and pyridine. Indoles with a pyridine ring fused in the 2,3-position are called carbolines: there are four isomers [e.g. 2-(or β-) carboline (41)].

II. RING SYNTHESES

1. General Survey
The important methods of synthesizing these five-membered heterocyclic rings are of two types: (*i*) those which involve C–Z bond formation only (42), and (*ii*) those which involve formation of the

42   43

C3–C4 bond (43). For easy reference, the methods of most practical importance are collected in the following table.

Ring synthesized	Synthesis		Section
	Type	Name	
Pyrroles	42	Paal-Knorr	4.II.2.*c.i*
	43	Knorr	4.II.3.*a*
	43	Hantzsch	4.II.3.*c*
Furans	42	Paal-Knorr	4.II.2.*c.ii*
	43	Feist	4.II.3.*c*
Thiophenes	42	Paal-Knorr	4.II.2.*c.iii*
Pyrrolidines Tetrahydrofurans Thiolanes	42	–	4.II.2.*a.i*
Indoles	42	Reissert	4.II.2.*c.iii*
	43	Bischler	4.II.3.*c*
	43	Fischer	4.II.3.*b*
Benzofurans Thionaphthenes	43	–	4.II.3.*d.ii*
Indoxyls	43	–	4.II.3.*d.i*
Oxindoles	43	Brunner	4.II.3.*b*
Indolenines	43	Fischer	4.II.3.*b*
Carbazoles	43	Graebe-Ullmann	4.II.3.*d.iv*
Tetrahydrocarbazoles	43	Borsche	4.II.3.*b*

2. Formation of C–Z Bonds

(*a*) *Saturated Compounds*

(*i*) Pyrrolidine (45, $Z = NH$) and thiolane (45, $Z = S$) can be prepared from tetramethylene dibromide (44), and tetrahydrofuran (45, $Z = O$) is obtained from the di-ol (46).

44   45   46   47   48

(*ii*) γ-Hydroxy- and γ-thiol-acids (47, $Z = O, S$) usually cyclize spontaneously to give lactones and thiolactones (48). γ-Amino-acids (47, $Z = NH$) require heating to effect lactam formation (48).

(*iii*) Pyrrolidines may also be prepared by Mannich reactions [e.g. the formation of tropinone by reaction (49 → 50)]; reactions of this type are involved in alkaloid biogenesis.

(*iv*) The synthesis of pyrrolidines by the free radical transformation of N-chloro derivatives (51 → 52) is of preparative significance.

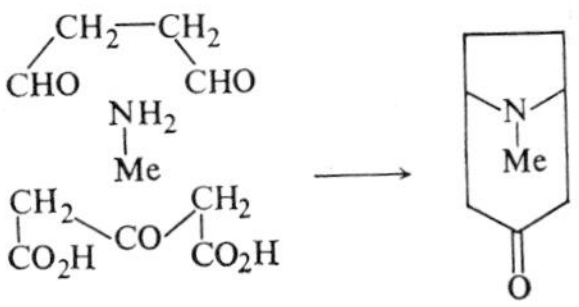

49   50 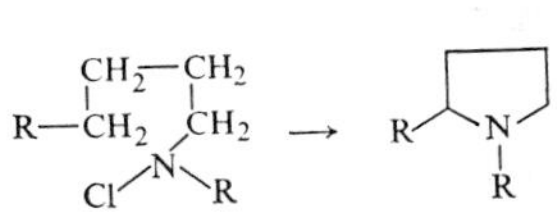   51   52

(*b*) *Rings with One Ethylenic Linkage.* Compounds with a 3,4-double bond (53, 54) or a 3,4-fused benzene ring (55, 56) can be prepared by methods analogous to those in (*a*) above (e.g. 57 → 58).

53 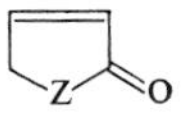   54 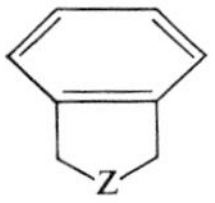   55 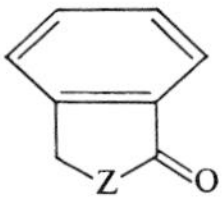   56

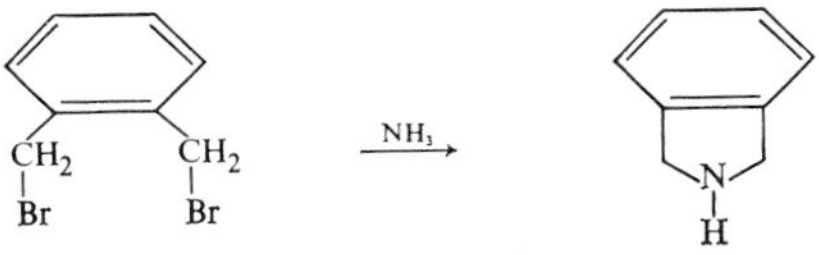

57   58

Compounds with a 2,3-double bond or a 4,5-benzo ring can be synthesized in the following ways.

(*i*) Cyclic enol-ethers are formed from γ-keto-alcohols [e.g. $Ac(CH_2)_3OH$ gives the dihydrofuran (59) on distillation].

(*ii*) β,γ-Unsaturated lactones are prepared from γ-keto-acids (e.g. 60 → 61).

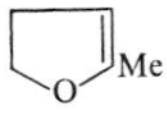

59 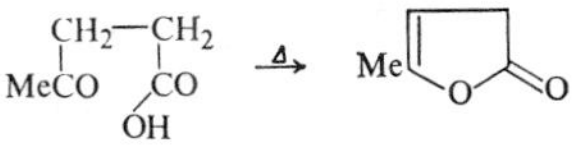   60   61

(*iii*) Indolines (63, Z = H) and their S- and O-analogues are prepared from *o*-substituted β-phenylethyl bromides (62) which cyclize either spontaneously or on heating or treatment with alkali.

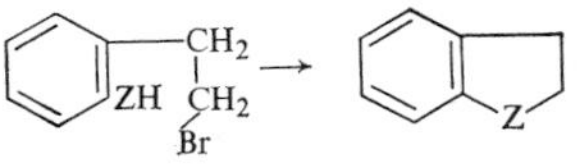

62   63 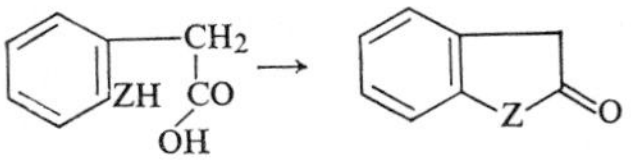   64   65

(*iv*) Oxindoles (65, Z = NH) are likewise formed by spontaneous cyclization of acids of type (64).

(*c*) *Aromatic Compounds.* The versatile Paal–Knorr synthesis is the most important preparative method for furans and thiophenes; it is also extensively used for pyrroles. The common starting materials are 1,4-diketones (e.g. 65a) which yield:

(*i*) Pyrroles (66, Z = NH or NR) by reaction with NH_3 or RNH_2.
(*ii*) Furans (66, Z = O) on treatment with H_2SO_4, P_2O_5, or $ZnCl_2$.
(*iii*) Thiophenes (66, Z = S) by distilling with P_4S_7.

65a   66 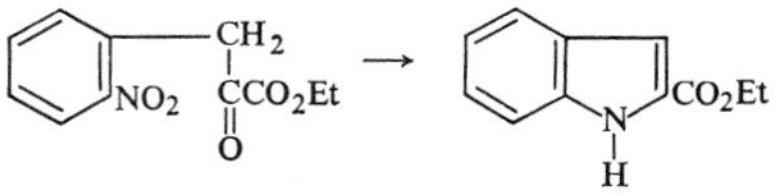   67   68

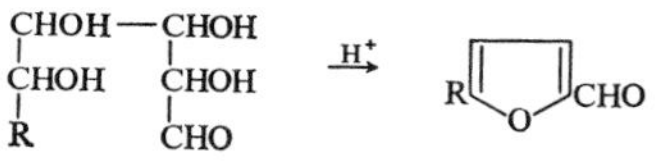

69   70

The Reissert indole synthesis is a related reaction. *o*-Nitrotoluene undergoes a Claisen condensation with oxalic ester to yield the pyruvic ester (67). When this is reduced with Zn–AcOH the corresponding amino derivative spontaneously cyclizes to 2-ethoxy-carbonylindole (68).

1,2,3,4-Tetrahydroxy compounds are used in further reactions of the same general type. Thus, hexoses (69, R = CH_2OH) and pentoses (69, R = H) give 5-hydroxymethylfurfural (70, R = CH_2OH) and furfural (70, R = H), respectively.

Pyrolysis of butane with sulphur gives thiophene; this reaction is probably the source of thiophene in coal-tar benzene.

3. Formation of the C3–C4 Bond

(*a*) *The Knorr Pyrrole Synthesis.* The Knorr pyrrole synthesis is the most important route to pyrroles. This versatile method involves the condensation of a β-keto-ester with an α-amino-ketone (e.g. 71 → 72). The β-keto-ester can be replaced by a β-diketone; simple ketones give poor yields. The amino-ketone is frequently prepared *in situ* by nitrosation and reduction (e.g. with Zn–AcOH) of a second mole of the β-keto-ester.

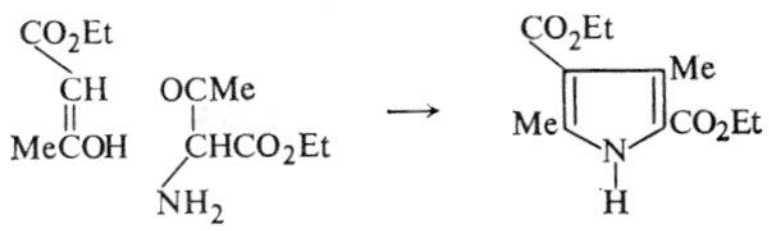

CO₂Et $\quad$ CO₂Et

71 $\qquad$ 72

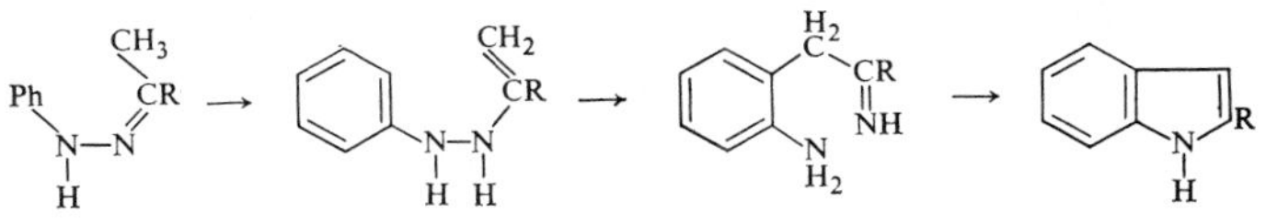

73 $\qquad$ 74 $\qquad$ 75 $\qquad$ 76

(*b*) *The Fischer Indole Synthesis.* The Fischer indole synthesis is the most important preparative method for indoles. The tautomeric form (74) of a phenylhydrazone (73) can undergo an *ortho*-benzidine-type rearrangement to give an intermediate (75) which spontaneously cyclizes by loss of ammonia to an indole (76). The reaction requires an acid catalyst (e.g. $ZnCl_2$, $HCl–H_2O$, H_2SO_4) and temperatures of *ca.* 100–200°.

If the phenylhydrazone contains both an α-methylene and an α-methyl group, the former reacts preferentially (e.g. 77 → 78). With a tertiary hydrogen atom on the α-carbon, as in, e.g. (79), an indolenine (80) is formed (in preference to an indole).

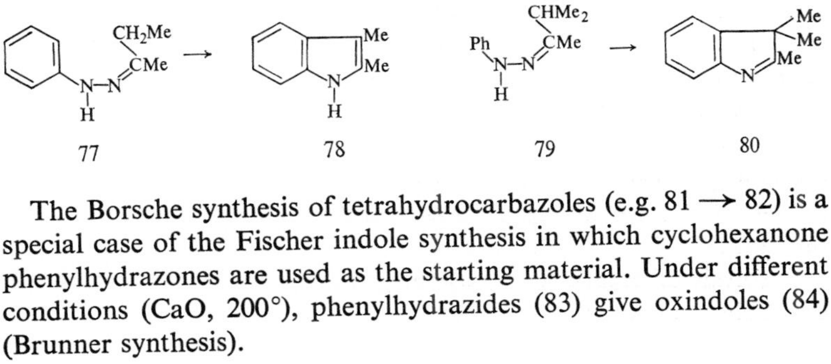

77 $\qquad$ 78 $\qquad$ 79 $\qquad$ 80

The Borsche synthesis of tetrahydrocarbazoles (e.g. 81 → 82) is a special case of the Fischer indole synthesis in which cyclohexanone phenylhydrazones are used as the starting material. Under different conditions (CaO, 200°), phenylhydrazides (83) give oxindoles (84) (Brunner synthesis).

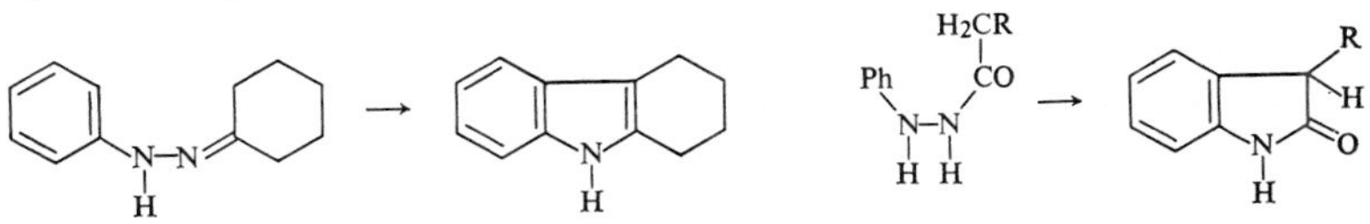

81 $\qquad$ 82 $\qquad$ 83 $\qquad$ 84

(*c*) *Cyclization of* α-*Halogeno-Ketones to give Pyrroles, Furans, and Indoles.* α-Halogeno-ketones react with:
  (*i*) Vinylamines to form pyrroles.

(*ii*) β-Keto-esters to give furans.

(*iii*) Anilines to yield indoles.

Two alternative orientations are possible. The orientation in the Hantzsch pyrrole synthesis (e.g. 85 → 86) differs from that in the Feist furan synthesis (e.g. 87 → 88). The Bischler indole synthesis yields mixtures of comparable amounts of the products arising from reaction of the aromatic amine with the halogeno-ketone in both possible orientations [e.g. $PhNH_2 + PhCOCH_2Br$ → (89) + (90)].

85   86   87   88

89   90

(*d*) Other Cyclizations onto a Benzene Ring

(*i*) Indoxyls and their oxygen and sulphur analogues are prepared by the cyclization of anilino-, phenoxy-, and phenylthio-acetic acids (91 → 92). The condensing agents used are $NaNH_2$ (for Z = NH), P_2O_5 (for Z = O), and H_2SO_4 (for Z = S).

(*ii*) Indoles, thionaphthenes, and benzofurans result from ketones of type (93) which are cyclized to (94, Z = NH, S, O) by $ZnCl_2$ or H_2SO_4.

(*iii*) Dibenzofurans and dibenzothiophenes (96) are formed by

91   92   93   94

95   96   97

spontaneous Pschorr-type cyclization of the diazonium salts
(95, Z = O, S).

(*iv*) Carbazoles are prepared by the Graebe-Ullmann synthesis.
Diazonium salts of type (95, Z = NH) spontaneously cyclize to the
benzotriazole (97). On pyrolysis these triazoles yield carbazoles
(96, Z = NH) (cf. Section **5.III.E.***b*).

III. REACTIONS OF THE AROMATIC NUCLEI

Electrophilic substitution of pyrrole, furan, and thiophene occurs
easily, and many examples are known; they are discussed in detail
in Sections **4.III.B.1–8**. A hydrogen on the pyrrole nitrogen atom can
be removed by nucleophilic reagents to give a reactive anion (see
Section **4.III.C.1**), and pyrroles, furans, and thiophenes can be
reduced (Section **4.III.C.2**). Other reactions with nucleophilic reagents are rare (Section **4.III.C.3**). Little is known about free radical
reactions (Section **4.III.C.4**). Furans and 3,4-benzo-pyrroles and
-thiophenes undergo Diels-Alder reactions (Section **4.III.C.5**), a sign
of their low aromaticity.

A. GENERAL SURVEY OF REACTIVITY

(*a*) *Comparison with Aliphatic Series.* Many common reactions of
aliphatic amines, ethers, and sulphides involve initial attack by an
electrophilic reagent at a lone pair of electrons on the heteroatom;
salts, quaternary salts, coordination compounds, amine oxides,
sulphoxides, and sulphones are formed in this way (98). Corresponding reactions are very rare (cf. Section **4.III.C.1**) with pyrroles, furans,
and thiophenes. These heterocycles react with electrophilic reagents
at the carbon atoms (99, 100) rather than at the heteroatom. Vinyl
ethers and amines (101) show intermediate behaviour, reacting
frequently at the β-carbon but sometimes at the heteroatom.

| 98 | 99 | 100 | 101 |

| 102 | 103 | 104 | 105 | 106 |

The heteroatoms of pyrrole, furan, and thiophene carry partial positive charges in the ground state which hinder reaction with electrophilic reagents. Conversely, the carbon atoms of these compounds are partially negatively charged, which aids reaction with electrophilic reagents at the ring carbons. This charge distribution follows from the valence bond theory as a consequence of contributions to the resonance hybrids of canonical forms (102) and (103). Molecular orbital theory leads to similar predictions: the heteroatom contributes two electrons to the π-molecular orbitals and the carbon atoms only one electron each (105). Similar considerations apply to the aliphatic analogues (cf. 104, 106).

$$\text{EtO}\overset{\frown}{-}\text{CH}\overset{\frown}{=}\text{CH}_2 \text{H}^+ \;\rightarrow\; \text{Et}\overset{+}{\text{O}}=\text{CH}-\text{CH}_2-\text{H} \;\rightarrow\; \text{Et}\overset{+}{\text{O}}=\text{CH}-\text{Me} \;\rightarrow\; \text{EtO}-\text{CH}-\text{Me}$$

107	108	109	110

(b) *Aromaticity.* Vinyl ethers and amines disclose little tendency to 'revert to type'; thus, the intermediate formed by reaction with an electrophilic reagent reacts further by adding a nucleophilic species to yield an addition compound [cf. the sequence (107 → 110)]. Thiophene and pyrrole have a high degree of aromatic character: appreciable resonance energies are measured by heats of combustion, and the NMR spectra indicate the existence of ring currents. Consequently, the initial product formed by reaction of thiophene or pyrrole with an electrophilic species subsequently loses a proton to give a substituted compound [cf. the reaction sequence (111 → 114)]. Furan has less aromatic character and often reacts by overall addition as well as by substitution.

111	112	113	114

115	116

The Kekulé resonance of the benzene ring is impaired in the 3,4-benzo derivatives (115), and these compounds are unstable and usually react by overall addition. 2,3-Benzo derivatives (116) have appreciable resonance energies and usually 'revert to type'.

B. REACTIONS WITH ELECTROPHILIC REAGENTS

1. Ease of Reaction

Electrophilic substitution is much easier than in benzene; thiophene reacts about as readily as mesitylene (*ca.* 10^3 times the rate of benzene); pyrrole and furan react as readily as phenol or even resorcinol.

The effect of substituents on the reactivity of heterocyclic nuclei is similar to that on benzene. Thus, one *meta*-directing substituent makes further substitution somewhat more difficult, and two make it very difficult indeed; e.g. 2,5-furandicarboxylic acid cannot be nitrated, sulphonated, or halogenated. Alkyl and aryl groups, halogens, and fused benzene rings have relatively little effect on the ease of substitution. Hydroxyl and amino groups should make substitution easier, however these compounds either exist in another tautomeric form or are highly unstable (see Section **4.V.1**), and little is known about their substitution reactions.

2. Orientation

Pyrrole, furan, and thiophene are always predominantly, and usually exclusively, substituted in the α-position. The transition state leading to *alpha* substitution (117) is evidently more stable than that leading to *beta* substitution (118). The tendency toward *alpha* substitution is strong; if an α-position is vacant, substitution is usually into it regardless of the directive influence of substituents already present.

117   118   119

The principal exception to this rule is that indole and thionaphthene are usually substituted in the β-position (119); here the transition state for *alpha* substitution involves disturbance of the benzene ring mesomerism. Curiously, benzofuran is substituted in the α-position (119). When both α-positions are vacant, substitution is directed by the substituent(s) already present (120); this also happens when the α-positions are substituted but both β-positions are vacant (121).

120   121

3. Nitration

Thiophene with nitric acid in acetic acid gives 70–85% 2- and 5% 3-nitrothiophene. Further nitration (HNO_3–H_2SO_4) of the mononitro derivatives occurs as expected [see diagrams (123) and (124)]. 2-Cyanothiophene is nitrated predominantly in the 4-position; the directive strength of the cyano group is evidently stronger than that of the thiophene ring.

Pyrrole and acetyl nitrate (HNO_3–Ac_2O) give 2-nitropyrrole in poor yield. 2-Acetyl- and 2-methoxycarbonyl-pyrrole, which are stabilized by electron-withdrawing substituents, can be nitrated to give mixtures of comparable amounts of the 4- and 5-nitro derivatives in better yields than those obtained from the parent compound.

Furan and acetyl nitrate give the addition compound (125) which is converted by pyridine into 2-nitrofuran. The positions in which substituted furans undergo nitration with acetyl nitrate are shown in diagrams (126)–(130) and illustrate the rules of orientation outlined in Section **4.III.B.2**.

4. Sulphonation

Thiophene readily gives the 2-sulphonic acid on shaking with sulphuric acid; benzene is usually freed from thiophene in this manner.

Pyrrole and furan are resinified by sulphuric acid (Section **4.III.B.9**), but the pyridine-sulphur trioxide complex (Section **2.IV.B.2**) gives pyrrole-, furan-, and thiophene-2-sulphonic acids in fair yields. Furan can be further sulphonated by this complex to give the 2,5-disulphonic acid.

5. Halogenation

Chlorine and bromine react with thiophene to give successively the halogenation products shown (131–134). The bromination can be interrupted at the intermediate stages; monochloro and dichloro derivatives have been obtained preparatively by chlorination with MeCONHCl. Addition products are also formed during chlorination; prolonged action (with Cl_2-I_2) gives the dihydrothiophene derivative (135, Z = S). Iodination (I_2-HgO) results in mono- and di-iodo-thiophenes (131, 132) only. Substituted compounds are halogenated as expected; see, e.g., structures (136) and (137).

| 131 | 132 | 133 | 134 | 135 |

| 136 | 137 |

Chlorination (SO_2Cl_2), bromination (Br_2-AcOH), and iodination (I_2-KI) of pyrrole all give the corresponding tetrahalogeno-pyrrole. In substituted pyrroles, all the vacant positions are usually sub-stituted. Prolonged chlorination (excess SO_2Cl_2) of pyrrole gives (135, Z = NH).

| 138 | 139 | 140 | 141 |

Furan decomposes under most conditions for halogenation, but with bromine, compounds (138)–(141) are formed successively, again illustrating the smaller aromaticity of furan and its greater tendency to form addition products than the S- or NH-analogues. Furans stabilized by electron-withdrawing groups are halogenated more smoothly; thus, 2-furoic acid is brominated to form successively the 5-monobromo and 4,5-dibromo derivatives (cf. 137).

6. Acylation

Thiophene is readily acylated under Friedel–Crafts conditions using mild catalysts (e.g. $SnCl_4$, $ZnCl_2$) to give normal products. Thus, acetyl chloride, benzoyl chloride, and succinic anhydride form the 2-acylthiophenes (142, Y = COMe, COPh, $COCH_2CH_2CO_2H$).

Furan and pyrrole react with acetic anhydride, even without a catalyst, to give the 2-acetylated products (143, Z = O, NH). Indole is similarly converted into its 1,3-diacetyl derivative (144). The Hoeben-Hoesch ketone synthesis is also applicable to the preparation of acyl derivatives of furans and pyrroles, e.g., ethyl 2,4-dimethyl-pyrrole-3-carboxylate with CH_3CN and HCl yields (145).

| 142 | 143 | 144 | 145 |

Aldehydes can be prepared by reaction of thiophenes, furans, and pyrroles with N-methylformanilide using $POCl_3$ as catalyst.

Pyrroles and furans also undergo the Gattermann aldehyde synthesis. This reaction involves treatment with HCl and HCN, and converts furan into furfuraldehyde and 2-methylindole into 2-methylindole-3-carboxaldehyde.

7. Reactions with Aldehydes and Ketones

(*a*) *Formation of Carbinols or Carbonium Ions.* When thiophenes, pyrroles, and furans react with the conjugate acids of aldehydes and ketones (146), the initial product is the alcohol (147). Usually this cannot be isolated as such because the hydroxyl group is readily lost to give a cation (148) (cf. Section **4.IV.3.***b*), which can be the end product or can react further.

| 146 | 147 | 148 | 149 |

If the cation (148) is stabilized by mesomerism, it is often the end product. In the Ehrlich test for pyrroles, *p*-dimethylaminobenzaldehyde and hydrochloric acid give brightly coloured products of type (149). As expected, pyrroles react preferentially in the α-position and indoles in the β-position, but if these positions are filled, reaction can occur at other sites.

(*b*) *Further Reactions of Carbonium Ions.*

(*i*) With non-N-substituted pyrroles, ions of type (148, Z = NH) can lose a proton from the ring nitrogen (e.g. indole with Ph_2CO or PhCHO in HCl–EtOH gives products of type 149a). Indole with

149a   150

HCO$_2$H or PhCOCl gives 'rosindoles' (150, R = H, Ph), involving the formation of ketones and a subsequent reaction of this type with a second molecule of indole (cf. discussion in Section 4.III.B.6).

151   152   153

(*ii*) The ion (148), acting as an electrophilic reagent, can also attack another molecule of the heterocyclic compound. Thiophene with benzaldehyde or chloral gives the binuclear product (151, R = Ph, CCl$_3$). Pyrrole and furan react with acetone to form tetranuclear derivatives of type (152, Z = NH, O). Pyrroles with only one free position react analogously to thiophene; e.g. two molecules of 3-ethoxycarbonyl-2,4-dimethylpyrrole with formaldehyde afford the dipyrromethane (153).

(*iii*) More rarely, ions of type (148) form dimeric products (possibly by initial loss of nuclear protons); thus, thiophenes with two free α-positions, or free adjacent α- and β-positions, give indophenines (e.g. 153a) with isatin (153b). This reaction is used as a test for thiophene, the so-called 'indophenine test'.

153a   153b

153c   153d   153e

(*c*) *Chloromethylation.* Chloromethylation of furans and thiophenes may be accomplished smoothly using formaldehyde and hydrochloric acid; an intermediate alcohol of type (147) is converted in a chloromethyl group. Thus, thiophene gives (153c) and thionaph-thene yields (153d). Furan is destroyed by this treatment, but 2,5-diphenylfuran, for example, gives the 3,4-bis-chloromethyl derivative (153e).

154   155

156   157

(*d*) **Mannich Reaction.** Mannich reactions involve the formation of CH_2:NR_2^+ ions from formaldehyde and an amine, which then react with the heterocyclic compound in a manner analogous to that indicated in diagram (146). These reactions occur readily with the heterocycles under consideration:

(*i*) Thiophene with $NH_3 + CH_2O \rightarrow$ (154).

(*ii*) Indole with $NHMe_2 + CH_2O \rightarrow$ gramine (155).

(*iii*) Tetrahydro-β-carbolines are synthesized by an internal Mannich reaction (e.g. 156 → 157) which is thought to be analogous to their biosynthesis.

8. Diazo-Coupling, Nitrosation, and Mercuration

(*i*) Diazonium ions couple with pyrroles and indoles to give products of type (158).

(*ii*) Nitrosation ($NaNO_2$–HOAc) of some pyrroles is successful [e.g. 3-methoxyindole gives (159)].

158   159   160   161

(*iii*) Mercuric acetate tends to mercurate all free nuclear positions in thiophenes and furans (cf. benzene, which gives mono- and *p*-di-acetoxymercuribenzene). Thiophene and furan themselves give products of type (160), and even deactivated dimethyl 2,5-furan-dicarboxylate gives (161).

Mercuric chloride, which is a milder reagent than mercuric acetate, does not react with benzene but forms 2-mono- and 2,5-di-mercurichloride derivatives from thiophenes and furans.

9. Reactions with Acids

(*a*) *Cation Function.* Pyrroles react with acids (162) to give unstable cations of type (163) or (164). Thiophenes and furans form similar ions as reaction intermediates. Proton loss reforms the original compound; all the ring hydrogen atoms of pyrroles exchange with deuterium in acid solution. The 1-hydrogen atoms of pyrroles exchange even in neutral solution, presumably *via* the anions (cf. Section 4.III.C.1).

$$\begin{array}{ccccc} & & & CH_2{-}CH_2 & CH_2{-}CH_2 \\ & & & CH \quad CH & MeOCH \quad CHOMe \\ 162 & 163 & 164 & NOH \; NOH & MeO \quad OMe \\ & & & 165 & 166 \end{array}$$

(*b*) *Ring Opening.* Initial protonation (cf. 162 → 163, 164) allows easy subsequent attack by nucleophilic reagents on pyrrole and furan. In these ring-opening reactions, cations formed by β-protonation (164) appear to be involved as intermediates. Thus, pyrrole with hydroxylamine gives succindialdoxime (165), and furan with methanolic hydrochloric acid yields the acetal (166).

(*c*) *Polymerization.* Protonation also induces polymerization. Pyrrole gives the trimer (167) and a high polymer 'pyrrole red'. Indole yields the dimer (168, Y = 3-indolyl) and the trimer (169, Y = 3-indolyl) which correspond formally to the products of aldol- and Knoevenagel-type reactions, respectively, of (170) with additional molecules of indole. On acid treatment furans give resins by extended polymerization.

$$\begin{array}{cccc} 167 & 168 & 169 & 170 \end{array}$$

(*d*) *Picrates.* Indoles and carbazoles give red picrates which are molecular complexes similar to those formed by naphthalene and other hydrocarbons.

10. Oxidation

(*a*) *Pyrroles and Furans*. Pyrroles and furans are easily oxidized; many of these compounds decompose to ill-defined products on exposure to air. Pyrroles are oxidized by chromic oxide to maleimides (171) with loss of any substituents in the 2- or 5-positions. Other oxidizing agents, such as H_2O_2, O_3, etc., form 'pyrrole blacks', which are ill-defined polymers. Oxidation of furan, by bromine or electrolytically, in alcoholic solution gives the corresponding 2,5-dialkoxy-2,5-dihydrofuran (172). Other oxidizing agents often cause virtually complete degradation of both pyrroles and furans.

171　　　　172

(*b*) *Indoles*. Indoles are also easily oxidized. Catalytic oxidation by air over platinum gives peroxides; e.g. (174) is obtained from tetrahydrocarbazole. These peroxides can be reduced to indolenine carbinols (173) or rearranged to dicarbonyl derivatives (174 $\rightarrow$ 175).

173　　　　　174　　　　　175

(*c*) *Thiophenes*. Thiophenes are reasonably stable to atmospheric oxidation and to many oxidizing agents in solution. Ozone attacks the C=C bonds; e.g. thionaphthene (176) yields *o*-mercaptobenzaldehyde (177).

176　　　177　　　　178　　　　179　　　　180

The reactions of peracids (AcO_2H, $PhCO_3H$) with thiophenes are rare examples of the attack of an electrophilic reagent at the sulphur atom. Thiophene itself gives the bimolecular product (178) by a Diels-Alder-type condensation of the intermediate sulphones (cf. Section **4.VI.2**). However, thiophenes polysubstituted with phenyl or methyl groups or bromine atoms, and also thionaphthenes and dibenzothiophenes, yield sulphones which can be isolated (e.g. 179).

Another example of attack on the ring sulphur atom by an electrophile is the recently reported reaction of thiophene with $Me_3O^+ BF_4^-$ to yield the S-methylthiophenium cation (180).

C. OTHER REACTIONS OF THE AROMATIC NUCLEI

1. Reactions Involving Deprotonation of Pyrroles

(*a*) *Pyrroles as Acids.* As discussed in Section 4.III.A.*a*, electron transfer to the ring carbon causes the nitrogen atom of pyrroles to be much less basic than that in secondary amines. For the same reasons, the NH group of pyrroles is acidic, and pyrrole itself is a weak acid of about the same strength as acetylene. The resulting ion reacts exceedingly readily even with weak electrophilic reagents at either carbon (181) or nitrogen (182); this behaviour is similar to that of the ambident anion from acetoacetic ester which shows alternative reactions (183, 184).

(*b*) *Pyrrole Grignard Reagents.* Pyrroles and indoles, as active hydrogen compounds, react with Grignard reagents to give hydrocarbons and new, largely ionic Grignard reagents derived from the pyrrole or indole (e.g. 185). Pyrrolyl- and indolyl-magnesium halides undergo many of the normal Grignard reactions to give 1- or 2-substituted pyrroles (cf. 181 and 182) or 1- or 3-substituted indoles (cf. the discussion in Section **4.III.B.2**). Mixtures of the N- and C-substituted products are often formed, the proportions of which are frequently altered by changing the solvent, temperature, or reagent.

Pyrrolylmagnesium bromide (185) reacts as follows:
(*i*) Alkyl halides give 2-alkylpyrroles (e.g. 186).
(*ii*) Chloroformic ester yields a mixture of (187) and (188).
(*iii*) Carbon dioxide gives mixtures of the 1- and 2-carboxylic acids.
(*iv*) Esters or acid chlorides yield mixtures of 1- and 2-acyl compounds.
Ketones and esters usually react further with Grignard reagents;

however, both ketones and esters of type (188) and pyrrolyl Grignard reagents are stabilized by mesomerism, and are therefore less reactive.

(*c*) *Further Pyrrole Anion Intermediates.* Pyrroles can be converted into alkali metal salts (with $NaNH_2$–NH_3 or K–$PhCH_3$), acylation and akylation of which give mainly 1-substituted derivatives.

In addition to Grignard reactions and those occurring through complete transformation into alkali metal salts, there are reactions which take place under conditions of only partial conversion into anions. 2-Substituted pyrroles and 3-substituted indoles result; the following exemplify reactions of this type:

(*i*) Boiling aqueous potassium carbonate converts pyrrole into its 2-carboxylic acid; the ion (181) reacts with carbon dioxide.

(*ii*) 2,3,4,5-Tetramethylpyrrole with MgO–MeI gives pentamethyl-pyrrolenine (189).

(*iii*) Alkyl nitrites or nitrates with sodium ethoxide convert indole into 3-nitroso- (e.g. 190 → 191) or 3-nitro-indoles, respectively.

189   190   191

192   193

(*iv*) Pyrrole with potassium hydroxide and chloroform gives a 2-pyrrolecarboxaldehyde by a normal Reimer-Tiemann reaction. 3-Chloropyridine (193) is formed as a by-product, probably by the sequence $CHCl_3$ → CCl_2 radical; CCl_2 radical + pyrrole → the cyclopropane intermediate (192); and (192) → (193). The Reimer-Tiemann reaction involves 2-dichloromethylpyrrole as an intermediate.

2. Catalytic and Chemical Reductions

(*i*) The catalytic hydrogenation of furans has been extensively studied. This applies especially to furfural (194), from which products (195–200) have been obtained by the use of selective catalysts under carefully controlled conditions.

(*ii*) Pyrroles are catalytically hydrogenated, with difficulty, successively to Δ^3-pyrrolines and pyrrolidines (cf. 201 $\longrightarrow$ 202 $\longrightarrow$ 203). Pyrroles are also rather difficult to reduce chemically; thus, sodium

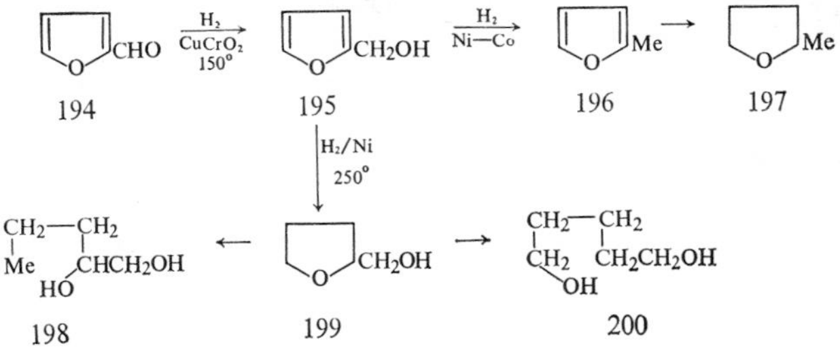

194   195   196   197

198   199   200

and ethanol usually have no effect, but zinc and acetic acid give Δ^3-pyrrolines (cf. 202).

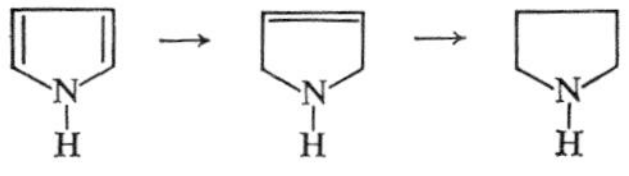

201   202   203

(*iii*) Thiophene can be reduced (Na–NH$_3$–MeOH) to a mixture of Δ^2- and Δ^3-dihydrothiophene together with butenethiols, which result from ring fission. With Raney nickel, thiophenes undergo desulphurization and simultaneous saturation of the ring carbon atoms instead of the normal catalytic reduction [e.g. (204) $\longrightarrow$ *n*-decanoic acid (205)]. Raney nickel desulphurization is used synthetically to build up long-chain compounds.

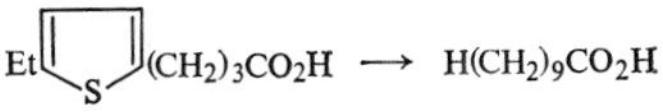

204   205

3. Other Reactions with Nucleophilic Reagents
Thiophene and furan with alkyl sodium compounds are metalated to form 2-sodio derivatives. These derivatives give salts of thiophene- and furan-2-carboxylic acid with carbon dioxide. 1-Substituted pyrroles can be similarly metalated in the 2-position.

4. Free Radical Reactions
Thiophene and furan are converted into 2-aryl derivatives by alkaline solutions of aryl diazonium salts. Pyrolysis of thiophene gives 2,2′-

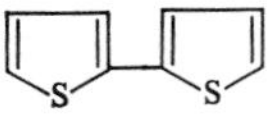

206 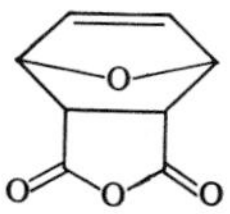   207

(206) and 3,3'-dithienyl. Other free radical reactions are little known or are of minor importance.

5. Diels-Alder Reaction

Monocyclic furans have sufficient diene character (i.e. low resonance energy) to react with active dienophiles. Thus furan with maleic anhydride yields (207). Examples of Diels-Alder reactions are also known with pyrroles, but thiophenes do not react. The furan nucleus is stabilized by a 2,3-benzo ring, and benzofurans do not undergo the Diels-Alder reaction.

3,4-Benzo rings exert a destabilizing effect, and isobenzofurans, isothionaphthenes, and isoindoles all react with dienophiles. Such reactions with maleic anhydride are illustrated by the transformations (208 → 209) and (210 → 211).

208   209   210   211

IV. REACTIONS OF SUBSTITUENTS ON AROMATIC NUCLEI

1. General Survey of Reactivity

In general, substituents on furans, thiophenes, and pyrroles react similarly to those on benzenoid nuclei, but there are some important differences:

(*i*) Some reactions requiring vigorous conditions which succeed in the benzene series fail because the heterocyclic rings are more susceptible to attack by electrophilic reagents (see Section **4.III.A**).

(*ii*) Amino or hydroxyl groups attached directly to the heterocyclic nuclei usually exist largely, or entirely, in an alternative, non-aromatic tautomeric form (see Section **4.V.**1), and their reactions show little resemblance to those in anilines or phenols.

(*iii*) Thienyl- and especially pyrryl- and furyl-methyl halides are more reactive than benzyl halides because the halogen is labilized by electronic shifts of the type Z—CH=CH—CH$_2$—Cl.

(*iv*) Hydroxymethyl and aminomethyl groups on heteroaromatic nuclei are activated in a manner similar to, although less marked than, the chloromethyl derivatives (see Section **4.IV.**3.*b*).

2. Fused Benzene Rings

Most of the common reactions of benzene rings involve attack by electrophilic reagents. Since thiophene, pyrrole, and furan are more readily attacked than benzene, reaction in fused-ring compounds should occur at a free position in the heterocyclic ring in preference to the benzene ring. This is generally true (see Sections **4.III.B.2–8** for examples). However, if the heterocyclic ring is strongly deactivated, reaction can occur on the benzo ring; e.g. bromination (Br_2) of 2-ethoxycarbonylbenzofuran (212) and nitration (KNO_3–H_2SO_4) of 3-nitrothionaphthene (213) occur as shown.

212   213

If the heterocyclic ring is tetra-substituted, electrophilic substitution reactions occur readily on the benzo ring. The dibenzo compounds can be considered to contain a diphenyl system together with a diphenyl ether, diphenylamine, or diphenyl sulphide system. On the basis of benzenoid chemistry the latter system would be expected to control the orientation, and indeed reaction in dibenzofuran, carbazole, and dibenzothiophene usually occurs *para* to the heteroatom (214) to give 3-mono- or 3,6-di-substituted compounds. This generally happens, as exemplified for:

(*i*) Dibenzofuran (214, Z = O): bromination (Br_2–CS_2), sulphonation ($ClSO_3H$), and formylation (HCN–HCl–$AlCl_3$).

(*ii*) Dibenzothiophene (214, Z = S): nitration (HNO_3–AcOH) and bromination (Br_2–CS_2).

214   215

(*iii*) Carbazole (214, Z = NH): acylation (RCOCl–$AlCl_3$), halogenation ($SOCl_2$ or Br_2–CS_2), and sulphonation (H_2SO_4).

For reasons which are not understood, dibenzofuran is nitrated (HNO_3–AcOH) successively in the 2- and 6-positions (cf. 215).

3. Alkyl and Substituted-Alkyl Groups

(*a*) *Alkyl Groups.* The reactivity of alkyl groups on heteroaromatic rings is similar to that of alkyl groups on benzenoid rings. Because of the high reactivity of the heterocyclic nuclei, few specific reactions of the alkyl groups are observed. Alkyl groups can be oxidized to carboxyl groups when the nucleus is stabilized by electron-attracting substituents (e.g. 216 → 217).

　216　　　　　　　　　217

When all nuclear carbon atoms carry substituents, halogenating agents of the free radical type halogenate methyl groups.

(*b*) *Substituted-Alkyl Groups: General.* As discussed in Section **4.IV.1**, halogenomethyl, hydroxymethyl, and aminomethyl groups show enhanced reactivity towards nucleophilic attack because of the ease with which the halogen, hydroxyl, or amino group is lost (218). In some cases nucleophilic reagents give isomeric products ($S_{N'}$ reaction) by the path shown (219 → 221) instead of those of normal replacement reactions.

　218　　　　219　　　　　　220　　　　　221

(*c*) *Halogenomethyl Groups.* The furfuryl halides (cf. 222, $Z = O$) are exceedingly reactive; they are usually not isolated but are used in solution as intermediates because of their instability. The halogen may be replaced directly by amino or alkoxyl groups, but with potassium cyanide the $S_{N'}$ product (223) is formed. 2-Bromomethyl-5-methylthiophene (cf. 222) gives normal replacement products with amines, but it is isomerized to (224) on attempted reaction with cuprous cyanide.

　222　　　　　223　　　　　224

(*d*) *Hydroxymethyl Groups.* Furfuryl alcohol (225) with hydrochloric acid gives laevulinic acid (227) *via* the $S_{N'}$ intermediate (226). The conversion of 2-furanacrylic acid (228) into an ester of γ-oxopimelic acid (229) by alcoholic hydrochloric acid is a related reaction involving an analogous intermediate (229a). 2-Thienylcarbinol reacts normally with hydrogen halides to give the 2-thienylmethyl halides (cf. 222, $Z = S$).

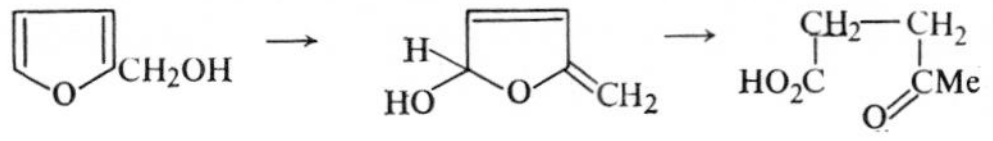

225 → 226 → 227

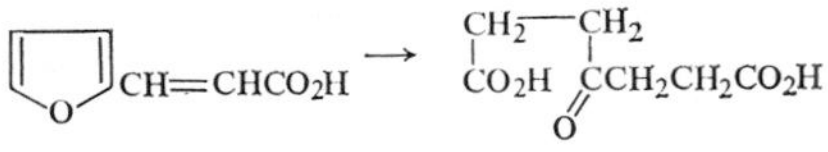

228 → 229

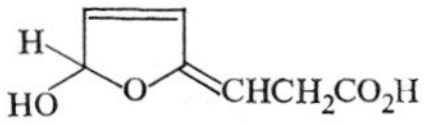

229a

(e) *Aminomethyl Groups.* The ready nucleophilic displacement of amino groups from aminomethyl compounds is useful in synthetic work. Thus, gramine (230, Y = NMe$_2$) reacts with various reagents to give other compounds of type (230):

(*i*) Potassium cyanide gives 3-indoleacetonitrile, which can in turn be reduced to tryptamine (230, Y = CH$_2$NH$_2$), or hydrolyzed to 3-indoleacetic acid (230, Y = CO$_2$H).

(*ii*) Diethyl acetamidomalonate gives (231), which can be hydrolyzed to tryptophan.

(*iii*) Nitroethane forms (230, Y = CHMeNO$_2$).

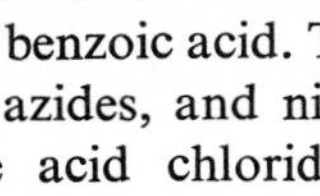

230

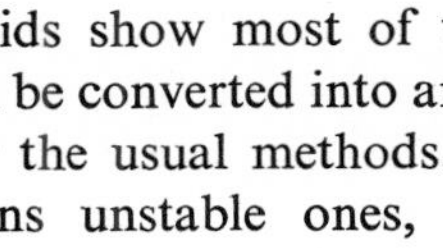

231

4. Carboxylic Acids

The heteroaromatic carboxylic acids show most of the standard reactions of benzoic acid. They can be converted into amides, esters, hydrazides, azides, and nitriles by the usual methods. Thiophenes form stable acid chlorides, furans unstable ones, and non-N-substituted pyrroles do not form them.

Furan- and pyrrole-2- and -3-carboxylic acids readily decarboxylate on heating to *ca.* 200°. Thiophenecarboxylic acids require higher temperatures or a copper-quinoline catalyst (cf. benzoic acid). In furans, α-groups are more readily lost than β-groups; thus, (232) and (233) both give initially furan-3-carboxylic acid. Decarboxylation often takes place during electrophilic substitution of the

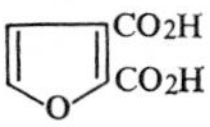

232

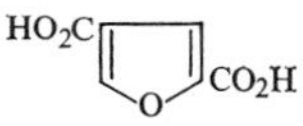

233

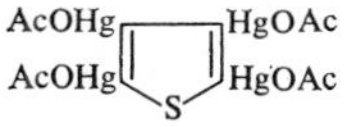

234

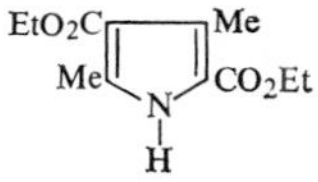

235

nucleus: thiophene-2-carboxylic acid and mercuric acetate give tetra-acetoxymercurithiophene (234).

In the pyrrole series, ester groups *alpha* to the nitrogen atom are more readily hydrolyzed by alkali, but those in the *beta* position more readily by acid. Thus, in compounds such as diethyl 2,4-dimethylpyrrole-3,5-dicarboxylate (235) either carbethoxy group may be selectively hydrolyzed and, if desired, subsequently eliminated by decarboxylation.

5. Formyl and Acyl Groups

(*i*) In reactions involving the formyl groups, pyrrole-, furan-, and thiophene-2- and -3-carboxaldehydes are all very similar to benzaldehyde. The biggest difference is shown by pyrrole-2-aldehyde, where the reactivity of the carbonyl group is reduced by mesomerism with the ring and the Cannizzaro and benzoin reactions do not occur.

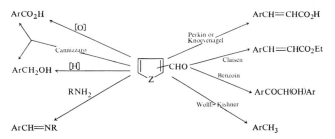

(*ii*) Ketones also behave similarly to their benzenoid analogues. However, some acyl groups are readily eliminated during electrophilic substitution as in the transformation of (236) into (237).

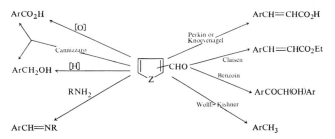

6. Halogen

Nuclear halogen atoms are chemically similar to those in phenyl and vinyl halides and usually do not undergo nucleophilic displacement reactions. However, they can be activated towards nucleophilic substitution by another substituent; e.g. 5-bromo-2-methoxy-carbonylfuran (238, Y = Br) reacts with NaOMe to form (238 Y = OMe).

Catalytic or chemical reduction replaces nuclear halogen atoms with hydrogen:

(*i*) 2,5-Dibromothiophene-3-sulphonic acid (239) with Na(Hg)–NaOH yields (240), illustrating a useful general method for the preparation of a 3-substituted derivative.

(*ii*) Tetraiodopyrrole + Zn–NaOH → pyrrole.

2-Bromothiophene and magnesium form 2-thienylmagnesium bromide which undergoes normal Grignard reactions to give:

(*i*) 2-Thiophenecarboxylic acid with CO_2.

(*ii*) 2-Thiophenecarboxyaldehyde with $HC(OEt)_3$.

(*iii*) 2-Thienylcarbinol with H_2CO.

2-Bromofuran requires an activated magnesium-copper alloy for conversion into the Grignard reagent, but 2-iodofuran reacts with magnesium; these Grignard reagents show normal reactions. Pyrroles form a different type of Grignard reagent (see Section **4.III.C.1.***b*).

7. Nitro, Sulphonic Acid, and Mercuri Groups

(*i*) 2- and 3-Nitrothiophenes are reduced by tin and hydrochloric acid to 2- and 3-aminothiophenes. Amino-pyrroles and -furans are too unstable to be isolated as such from the corresponding reaction mixtures; thus, 2-nitrobenzofuran (241) yields (242).

(*ii*) Thiophene-2-sulphonic acid is a strong acid, similar to benzene-sulphonic acid, which forms a sulphonyl chloride (with $POCl_3$) that undergoes typical reactions, e.g. reduction to thiophene-2-sulphinic acid (with zinc).

(*iii*) Mercury derivatives of thiophene and furan undergo reactions analogous to those observed in the benzene series as exemplified by the reaction scheme (formulae 243–248, Z = S, O).

8. N-Substituents on Pyrroles
N-Alkyl, N-aryl, and N-acyl groups on pyrroles migrate to the 2-position on pyrolysis as illustrated by (249 → 250) and (251 → 252). N-Acyl-pyrroles are very easily hydrolyzed (NaOH–H_2O at 20°).

$$
\begin{array}{ccccccc}
\underset{\underset{249}{\text{Ph}}}{\boxed{\text{N}}} & \xrightarrow{700°} & \underset{\underset{250}{\text{H}}}{\boxed{\text{N}}}\text{Ph} & \qquad & \underset{\underset{251}{\text{Ac}}}{\boxed{\text{N}}} & \xrightarrow{250°} & \underset{\underset{252}{\text{H}}}{\boxed{\text{N}}}\text{Ac}
\end{array}
$$

V. REACTIONS OF HYDROXYL, AMINO, AND RELATED COMPOUNDS

1. Survey of Reactivity
(*a*) *General.* Hydroxyl derivatives of thiophene, pyrrole, and furan (253 and 256) are tautomeric with alternative non-aromatic carbonyl forms (254, 255, and 257). Amino and mercapto derivatives are similarly tautomeric with imines (e.g. 258 ⇌ 259) and thiones (260 ⇌ 261), respectively. In the 'enolic' form (253 or 256), the reactivity of these compounds towards electrophilic reagents should be even greater than that of the parent heterocycles. It is therefore not unexpected that the monocyclic hydroxy- and amino-thiophenes, -pyrroles, and -furans are difficult to prepare, very unstable, and little known; most of the examples in this section are concerned with the more accessible benzo derivatives.

$$
\underset{253}{\boxed{\text{Z}}\text{OH}} \rightleftharpoons \underset{254}{\boxed{\text{Z}}\text{O}} \rightleftharpoons \underset{255}{\boxed{\text{Z}}\text{O}} \qquad \underset{256}{\boxed{\text{Z}}^{\text{OH}}} \rightleftharpoons \underset{257}{\boxed{\text{Z}}^{\text{O}}}
$$

$$
\underset{258}{\boxed{\text{Z}}\text{NH}_2} \rightleftharpoons \underset{259}{\boxed{\text{Z}}\text{NH}} \qquad \underset{260}{\boxed{\text{Z}}^{\text{SH}}} \rightleftharpoons \underset{261}{\boxed{\text{Z}}^{\text{S}}}
$$

(*b*) *Tautomerism of Monocyclic Compounds.* The proportions of the tautomers present at equilibrium depend on the relative stabilities of the two forms. The enol forms (253 or 256) possess the aromatic resonance energy of the ring. Carbonyl forms (254) and (255) have

the resonance energies of thioester, amide, or ester groups (cf.
262 ↔ 263), whereas carbonyl forms of type (257) have the resonance
energy due to a vinylogous thioester, amide, or ester group (cf.
264 ↔ 265).

262   263   264   265

Physical evidence (spectra, cf. Section 7.6) shows that α-hydroxy-
furans exist almost entirely as unsaturated γ-lactones (254 and 255,
$Z = O$). Both α,β- (254, $Z = O$) and β,γ-unsaturated lactones (255,
$Z = O$) are known; they are converted (e.g. by NEt_3) into an equilibrium mixture containing mainly the former. β-Hydroxyfurans
appear to exist at equilibrium as comparable amounts of both isomers
(e.g. 266 ⇌ 267). Electron-withdrawing groups and hydrogen bonding can stabilize the hydroxy forms, as in (268).

266   267   268

Recent spectroscopic evidence, mainly IR and NMR, has revealed
a similar pattern for the corresponding pyrroles and thiophenes. The
α-hydroxy derivatives exist as mixtures of the two carbonyl forms
(254) and (255), whereas the β-hydroxy compounds consist of equilibrium mixtures of the hydroxy (256) and carbonyl forms (257).

(c) *Tautomerism of Benzo Derivatives.* The alternative tautomeric
forms of monohydroxy-monobenzo compounds are shown (formulae
269–274). The aromatic resonance energy in 3,4-benzo derivatives
of type (273) does not exceed that of benzene (cf. Section 4.III.A.b);
thus, they exist completely in form (274). In compounds (269) and
(271), the additional aromatic resonance energy due to the fused
heterocyclic ring is appreciable for both types, but conjugation between the heteroatom and carbonyl group is less for the β- (272) than
for the α-derivative (270). Potential α-hydroxy compounds of type
(269) exist very largely in the carbonyl form (270), whereas the
β-derivatives (271) co-exist in both forms (271) and (272).

(d) *Interconversion and Reactivity of Tautomeric Forms.* Interconversion of the hydroxyl and carbonyl forms of these heterocycles

proceeds through an anion (as 276) or a cation (as 279), just as the enol (277) and keto forms (282) of acetone are interconverted through the ions (278) or (281). Reactions of the various species derived from the heterocyclic compounds are analogous to those of the corresponding species from acetone: hydroxyl forms react with electrophilic reagents (283) and carbonyl forms with nucleophilic reagents (284). In addition, either form can lose a proton (285, 286) to give an anion which reacts very readily with electrophilic reagents on either oxygen (287) or carbon (288).

It is also convenient to consider in this section the reactions of compounds of types (289)–(292). Compounds of types (289) and (290) bear a formal structural resemblance to quinones but show little similarity in their properties; this is to be expected in view of the dissimilarity of dihydroxy-benzenoid and dihydroxy-heterocyclic compounds.

2. Reactions with Electrophiles

(a) *Hydroxy Compounds.* Electrophilic substitution reactions at low pH values probably involve the hydroxyl form:

(i) Nitrosation ($NaNO_2$–H_2O–HCl), which gives tautomeric products (e.g. 295 → 294 ⇌ 293, Z = NH, O, S).

(ii) Coupling with diazonium salts (295 → 296).

293   294   295   296

297

(iii) Oxidation. Indoxyl and thioindoxyl (295, Z = NH, S) are very easily oxidized, e.g. by $K_3Fe(CN)_6$, to indigo (297) and thio-indigo, respectively, possibly *via* dimerization of free radical intermediates.

(b) *Anions.* These heterocyclic anions undergo many reactions which are similar to those of the acetone enolate anion.

(i) Claisen condensations with esters (298 → 299).

298   299   300   301

(ii) Carbon or oxygen alkylation by alkyl halides (300, 301). Alkylation of indoxyl (303, Z = NH) gives (302) or (304) as shown.

302   303   304

(iii) Aldol condensation with aldehydes and ketones to give hydroxy compounds (305 → 307) which usually spontaneously lose water (by a reverse Michael addition) to give unsaturated compounds (308). In this way anions derived from oxindole (309,

$Z = NH$) and indoxyl (303, $Z = NH$) react with isatin (310) to give isoindigo (311) and indirubin (312).

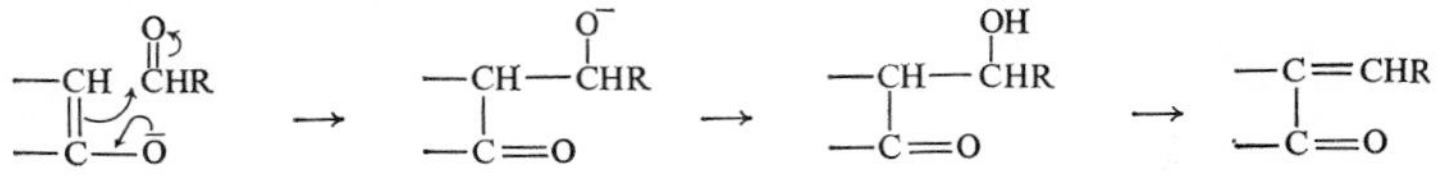

305   306   307   308

309   310

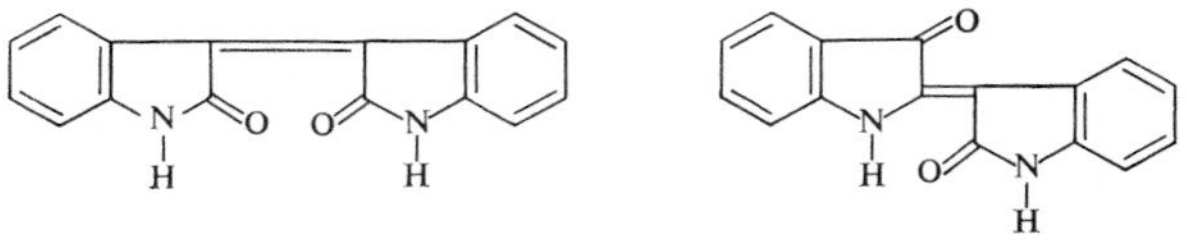

311   312

3. Reactions of Carbonyl Compounds with Nucleophiles

Nucleophilic reagents attack the carbonyl carbon atom; the subsequent course of this reaction parallels that in aliphatic chemistry. If the carbonyl group and the heteroatom are adjacent, the ring is usually opened (313 → 315). If they are not adjacent, a carbonyl addition compound (316 → 318) results, which often eliminates water spontaneously to give (319). The reactions of carbonyl groups in both environments are discussed.

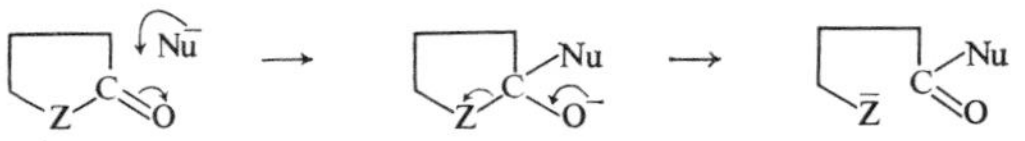

313   314   315

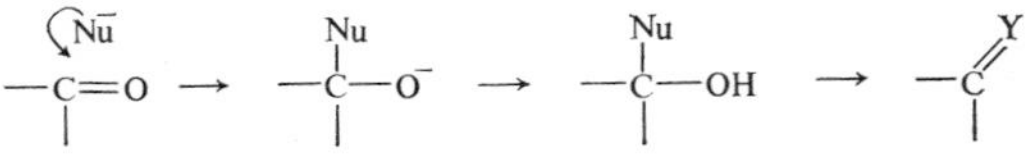

316   317   318   319

a) *Carbonyl Groups Adjacent to the Heteroatom.* Ring opening by nucleophilic reagents necessitates group Z gaining a negative charge, the ease of which depends on the heteroatom (S > O >> NH) and on the ring type (e.g. 320 > 321 > 322).

(*i*) Succinic, maleic, and phthalic anhydrides and imides (320, 323, 324, $Z = O$, NH) behave similarly to acyclic acid anhydrides and imides.

(*ii*) The ring opening of phthalimides (324, Z = NR) by hydrazine to give a primary amino compound and 1,4-phthalazinedione (325) (Ing-Manske reaction) is important in the modified Gabriel synthesis.

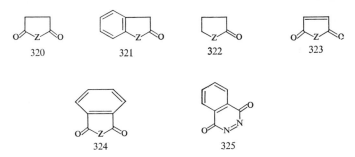

(*iii*) 2-Coumaranone (321, Z = O), its S-analogue (321, Z = S), and the diones (326, Z = O, S) react reversibly with hydroxide and alkoxide ions to give salts (as 327) and esters (as 328) of the ring-opened acid.

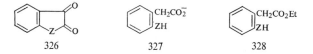

(*iv*) The corresponding reactions with oxindole (321, Z = NH) are much more difficult, but in the case of isatin (326, Z = NH), the second carbonyl group facilitates ring fission; e.g. treatment of (326) with sodium hydroxide gives sodium isatinate (cf. Pfitzinger reaction, Section **2.II.C.1.**a).

(*b*) *Carbonyl Groups Not Adjacent to the Heteroatom.* Carbonyl groups not adjacent to a heteroatom are less stabilized by resonance (cf. Section **4.V.1**) and react with the relatively weakly nucleophilic 'ketonic' reagents. If carbonyl groups of both types are present, as in (329, Z = O, NH), then the carbonyl group not adjacent to the heteroatom is preferentially attacked. Thus, isatin and indoxyl and their O- and S-analogues (329, 331) react with hydroxylamine, phenylhydrazine, etc. to give oximes, phenylhydrazones, etc. (329 → 330; 331 → 332).

The reactive 3-carbonyl group in compounds of type (329) under-goes aldol condensation with active methylene compounds; such reactions of isatin with indoxyl, oxindole, and dioxindole are men-tioned in Section **4.V.2.**b. The reaction of isatin with thiophenes is similar (cf. Section **4.III.B.7.**b).

4. Reduction of Carbonyl and Hydroxyl Compounds

In cyclic anhydrides and imides, one carbonyl group is usually easily reduced; thus, phthalic anhydride gives phthalide (333 → 334), and phthalimides yield phthalamides (335 → 336). Indoxyl and its O- and S-analogues can be reduced (Zn–HOAc) to indole, etc.

333   334   335   336

5. Reactions at Other Sites in the Ring

Carbon–carbon double bonds can be oxidized to carbonyl groups; thus, indigo and thioindigo (337, Z = NH, S) give isatin and thio-isatin (329) (with dilute HNO_3–H_2O, CrO_3, $KMnO_4$, O_3).

Carbon-carbon double bonds can be reduced: for example, indigo (337, Z = NH) gives indigo white (338 ⇌ 339) (with Fe^{++}–OH^-; Zn–H^+); thioindigo reacts analogously.

337   338   339

340   341   342

Ring imino groups can be alkylated and acylated; thus, isatin gives the acetyl derivatives (340) with acetic anhydride, and N-methylisatin (341) by methylation of the potassium or sodium salt. Methylation of the silver salt yields O-methylisatin (342).

Fused benzene rings can undergo electrophilic substitution reac-tions. Isatin (329, Z = NH) and oxindole (309, Z = NH) are nitrated, halogenated, and sulphonated *ortho* and *para* to the nitrogen atom under mild conditions. Indigo (337, Z = NH) reacts similarly except that nitration fails because of concomitant oxidation.

6. Amino and Imino Compounds

Free amino compounds are often very unstable and decompose rapidly. Potentially tautomeric compounds react in both the amino (343) and imino forms (344), but physical evidence, where available, indicates that the amino form predominates.

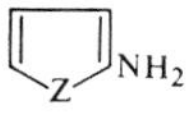

343 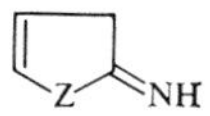   344 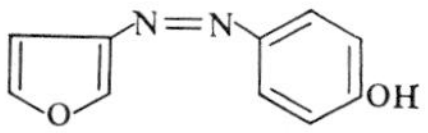   345

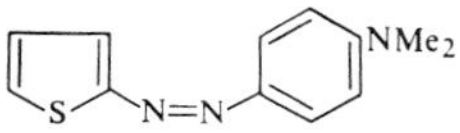

346 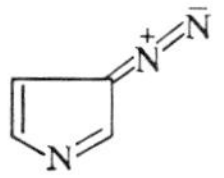   347 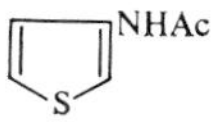   348

Amino compounds can be converted into diazonium salts which give coupled products (e.g. 345 and 346); replacement reactions of the Sandmeyer type often fail. Diazotization of pyrroles with a free NH group forms diazo-anhydrides of type (347). Acylation of the amino compounds gives stabilized acylamino derivatives (e.g. 348).

VI. REACTIONS OF OTHER NON-AROMATIC COMPOUNDS

Before turning to the dihydro and tetrahydro derivatives of the fundamental ring systems, two special classes of compounds are considered. The pyrrolenines and the thiophene sulphones both contain two double bonds in the heterocyclic ring, but in each case the conjugation does not include all the ring atoms.

1. Pyrrolenines and Indolenines

The chemistry of the indolenines (e.g. 349 and 353) is better known than that of the pyrrolenines and is the source of the examples given

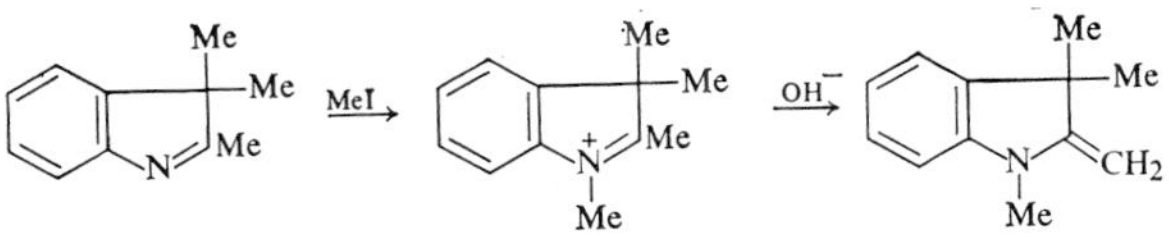

349   350   351

352   353   354

355   356

here; however, the discussion also applies to derivatives of the pyrrolenines (355 and 356).

The indolenines are much stronger bases than indoles confirming
that tautomerism between an indolenine and an indole strongly
favours the indole (cf. Section 7.4). Indolenines form stable hydrochlorides and quaternary salts (e.g. 350); the latter give anhydro
derivatives (351) on treatment with alkali.

Prolonged action of acid on indolenines unsubstituted in the 2-
position (e.g. 353) gives indoles (353 → 354) (Plancher rearrangement). Indolenines may be reduced to indolines (353 → 352).

2. Thiophene Sulphones

Thiophene sulphones show no aromatic character. They behave as
dienes and also show the reactions of compounds containing a $C=C$
bond conjugated with an electron-withdrawing group. Thiophene
sulphone itself is highly unstable, but alkyl and aryl substituents and
fused benzene rings increase the stability.

Thiophene sulphones undergo Diels-Alder reactions which are
followed by spontaneous loss of sulphur dioxide from the products;
e.g. thiophene sulphone (357) yields (358). Reducing agents (e.g.
Zn–HCl) convert the sulphones into thiophenes; this should be contrasted to the resistance of normal sulphones to reduction.

357   358   359   360

Recently, 1,1-dimethylindolium salts (360) have been prepared
(from 359) by dehydration. They are unstable, readily losing a
methyl group.

3. Dihydro Compounds

There are two possible types of dihydro-furans and -thiophenes (cf. 361 and 362), and examples of both are known. Non-N-substituted Δ^2-pyrrolines (362, Z = NH) tautomerize spontaneously to the Δ^1-compounds (363).

361   362   363

These dihydro compounds are usually readily aromatized; the following reactions illustrate some of the possible routes:

(*i*) Dehydrogenation; indoline (364, Z = NH) + chloranil → indole.

(*ii*) Retro-Diels-Alder reaction with loss of ethylene; (365) on pyrolysis yields, 3,4-diethoxycarbonylfuran.

(*iii*) Loss of acetic acid; (366) → 2-nitrofuran.

(*iv*) Disproportionation; Δ^3-pyrroline heated over platinum → pyrrole + pyrrolidine.

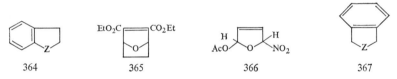

364   365   366   367

In their other reactions, these compounds resemble their aliphatic analogues. Thus, when Z is NH, (362) behaves as a vinylamine, (361) as an allylamine, (367) as a benzylamine, (364) as an aromatic amine, and (363) acts as a Schiff's base. Similar comparisons apply when Z is oxygen or sulphur: (364, Z = O) is an aromatic ether; (367, Z = O) is a dibenzyl-type ether; and (364, Z = S) is an aromatic sulphide.

4. Tetrahydro Compounds

Tetrahydrofurans, tetrahydrothiophenes, and pyrrolidines are cyclic ethers, sulphides, and amines, respectively. Their reactions can in general be readily deduced from a knowledge of aliphatic chemistry.

Five-Membered Rings Containing Two or More Heteroatoms

I. NOMENCLATURE AND IMPORTANT COMPOUNDS

1. Monocyclic Compounds Containing Annular Nitrogen Atoms Only

The structures and names of the five-membered rings containing two or more nitrogen atoms are shown in diagrams (1)–(6). Two aromatic tautomeric forms are possible for unsymmetrically substituted pyrazoles and imidazoles (e.g. $7 \rightleftharpoons 8$). Two or three (in unsymmetrically substituted compounds) aromatic tautomeric forms are possible for 1,2,3- and 1,2,4-triazoles and tetrazoles (cf. Section 5.III.A.2).

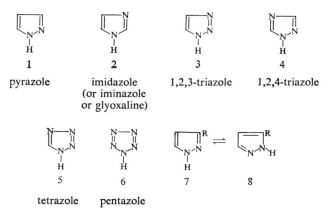

1	**2**	**3**	**4**
pyrazole	imidazole (or iminazole or glyoxaline)	1,2,3-triazole	1,2,4-triazole

5	**6**	**7** **8**
tetrazole	pentazole	

Some pyrazoles are used pharmaceutically, e.g. antipyrine (9).

Many imidazoles are important biologically:

(*i*) Histidine (10, Y = CO_2H) is an essential amino-acid.

(*ii*) Histamine (10, Y = H) occurs in ergot and in putrefied proteins; among its many physiological effects is thought to be the development of allergies in humans, hence the importance of 'antihistamines'.

(*iii*) Allantoin (11) is the end-product of nitrogen metabolism in some animals.

(*iv*) Pilocarpine (12) exemplifies the imidazole alkaloids.

9	10	11
antipyrine	histidine	allantoin
(an antipyretic	($Y = CO_2H$)	
and analgesic)	histamine	
	($Y = H$)	

12	13
pilocarpine	nitron
(alkaloid)	

Nitron (13), a triazolium betaine, forms an insoluble nitrate which is used analytically.

2. Monocyclic Compounds Containing Annular Nitrogen and Oxygen or Sulphur Atoms

By convention, oxazole and thiazole are used to name compounds with the heteroatoms in the 1,3-positions (14, $Z = O$, S) and isoxazole and isothiazole for the 1,2-isomers (15, $Z = O$, S). Four oxadiazoles and four thiadiazoles are possible: the 1,2,3-, 1,2,4-, 1,2,5-, and 1,3,4-isomers. Oxadiazolium betaines of type (16) are named sydnones, and 1,2,4-oxadiazoles, 1,2,5-oxadiazoles, and 1,2,5-oxadiazole 2-oxides are often called azoximes, furazans, and furoxans, respectively.

14	15	16	17
oxazole ($Z = O$)	isoxazole ($Z = O$)		cycloserine
thiazole ($Z = S$)	isothiazole ($Z = S$)		(antibiotic)

Important compounds include:

(*i*) Cycloserine (17), one of the few naturally occurring isoxazole derivatives.

(*ii*) Vitamin B$_1$ or thiamine (18, Y = H) and penicillin (see Section **6.II.A.1**), which are important naturally occurring thiazole and thiazolidine derivatives. Thiamine pyrophosphate (18, Y = P$_2$O$_6$H$_3$) is the coenzyme cocarboxylase.

(*iii*) Sulphathiazole (19).

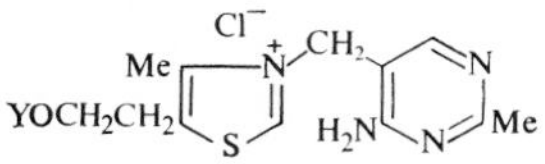

18

vitamin B$_1$ (Y = H)
cocarboxylase (Y = P$_2$O$_6$H$_3$)

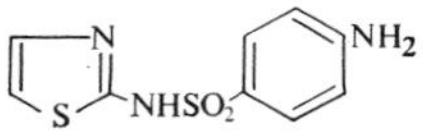

19

sulphathiazole
(bactericide)

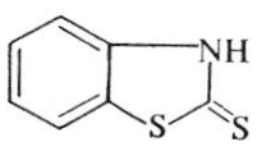

20

3. Polycyclic Derivatives

2-Benzothiazolethione, usually called 2-mercaptobenzothiazole (20), is an accelerator for rubber vulcanization; saccharin (21) is a sweetening agent. Indazole is the trivial name for the benzopyrazole nucleus (22), and anthranil for (23).

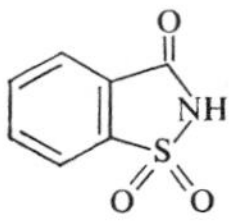

21

saccharin

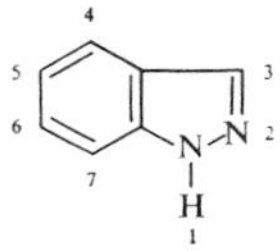

22

indazole

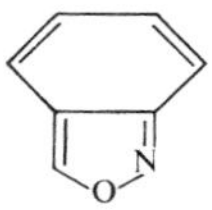

23

anthranil

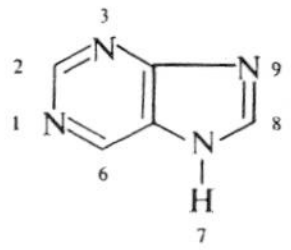

24

purine

The fused pyrimidine-imidazole nucleus (24) is called purine. Purines are widely distributed in nature.

(*i*) Uric acid (25) is the end-product of nitrogen metabolism in many animals.

(*ii*) Caffeine (26, R = R′ = Me), theobromine (26, R = H, R′ = Me), and theophylline (26, R = Me, R′ = H) are the active alkaloids of coffee, cocoa, and tea.

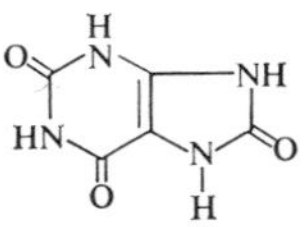

25

uric acid

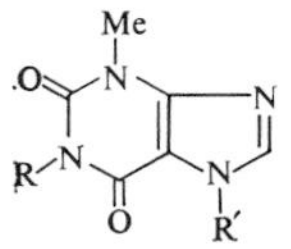

26

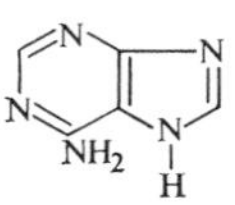

27

adenine

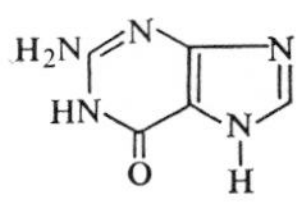

28

guanine

(*iii*) Adenine (27) and guanine (28) occur in all nucleic acids (cf. Section 3.I.1.*a*) in the form of nucleotides. A sugar phosphate residue is attached to the 9-position of these bases in the nucleotides. Adenosine mono-, di-, and tri-phosphate (AMP, ADP, ATP; 29, Y = H, PO_3H_2, $P_2O_6H_3$) are biologically important nucleotides.

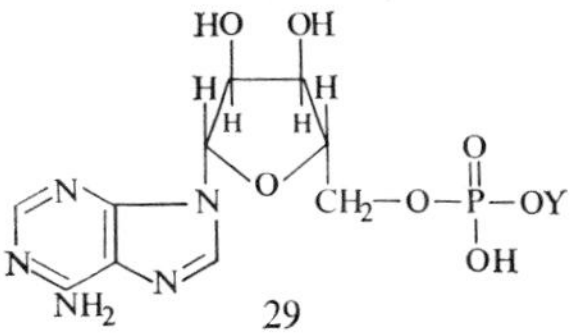

29

II. RING SYNTHESES

Ring syntheses are classified according to the number of heteroatoms in the ring and their relative orientation. Methods for the synthesis of compounds with heteroatoms in the 1,2- (30), 1,3- (31), 1,2,3- (32), 1,2,4- (33), 1,2,3,4- (34), and 1,2,3,4,5-positions (35) are considered successively.

30   31   32   33   34   35

A. HETEROATOMS IN THE 1,2-POSITIONS

1. Monocyclic Compounds

(*i*) The standard syntheses for pyrazoles (36) and isoxazoles (38) involve the reaction of β-dicarbonyl compounds (37) with hydrazines and hydroxylamine, respectively. These reactions take place under mild conditions and are of very wide applicability; the substituents Y can be H, R, Ar, CN, CO_2Et, etc.

(*ii*) Pyrazolones and isoxazolones* are prepared from β-keto-esters and hydrazine or hydroxylamine by reactions similar to those in (*i*) above (39 → 40).

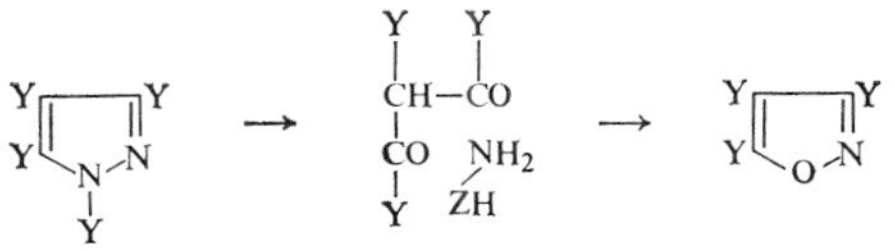

36   37   38

---

* The tautomerism of these compounds is considered in Section 5.IV.4.

39   40   41   42

(*iii*) α,β-Unsaturated ketones form pyrazolines and isoxazolines (41 → 42); the intermediate hydrazones and oximes are often isolated in these cases.

(*iv*) Tetrahydro compounds can be obtained from 1,3-dibromides (with N_2H_4, NH_2OH, $S_2^=$, etc.).

43   44   45   46

47   48   49   50

(*v*) Acetylenes add nitrile oxides and diazoalkanes to give isoxazoles (44 → 43) and pyrazoles (44 → 45), respectively. If an olefin is used instead of an acetylene, the non-aromatic analogues (46, Z = NH, O) result; yields are best when the olefin contains an electron-withdrawing substituent. These are examples of '1,3-dipolar additions', a reaction shown in generalized form in structures (47) and (48). Many azole derivatives can be prepared by reactions of this type.

(*vi*) Isothiazoles (50) may be obtained by the cyclization of β-thioxo-imines (49).

2. Benzo Derivatives

(*i*) Indazoles (51) are formed by spontaneous cyclization of *o*-acylphenylhydrazines (52, Z = NH). Certain *o*-toluenediazonium salts cyclize spontaneously to indazoles, but the yields are good only

51   52   53

when the methyl group is activated by an *ortho* or *para* electron-withdrawing group (54 → 55, probably *via* 56).

(*ii*) Anthranils (53) are formed from *o*-acylphenylhydroxylamines (52, Z = O) by cyclizations analogous to those in (*i*).

(*iii*) Benzisothiazoles (58) are prepared from sulphenyl chlorides (57).

(*iv*) Saccharins are obtained by $KMnO_4$ oxidation of *o*-methylbenzenesulphonamides (59 → 60).

B. HETEROATOMS IN THE 1,3-POSITIONS

1. Oxazoles, Thiazoles, and Imidazoles

(*i*) α-Halogeno-ketones react with amides (100°, no solvent), thioamides (reflux in EtOH), and amidines to give oxazoles, thiazoles, and imidazoles (61 → 62, Z = O, S, NH), respectively. This is the most important thiazole synthesis, and both the thioamide and the halogeno-ketone components can be varied widely.

(*ii*) α-Amino-ketones (63) react with imino-esters to give imidazoles (63 → 64).

(*iii*) Oxazoles and thiazoles are prepared by cyclization of α-acylamino-ketones: (65) + H_2SO_4 → (66, Z = O); (65) + P_2S_5 → (66, Z = S). In an analogous reaction, dithiolium salts (68) are prepared from α-dithioacyl-ketones (67).

$$\underset{65}{\overset{\displaystyle \text{RCH-NH}}{\underset{\displaystyle \text{RCO}\quad\text{COR}}{|\qquad|}}} \longrightarrow \underset{66}{\overset{R}{\underset{R}{\boxed{}_Z}}N}R \qquad \underset{67}{\overset{\text{CH}_2-\text{S}}{\underset{R}{\overset{C}{\diagdown}_O \; S \overset{C}{\diagup}}}R} \quad\overset{\text{H}^+}{\longrightarrow}\quad \underset{68}{\overset{R}{\boxed{}_S}^{S^+}}R$$

2. Other Monocyclic Derivatives

(*i*) β-Hydroxy-, β-amino-, and β-mercapto-acylamines (69, Z = O, NH, S) cyclize to give Δ²-oxazolines, Δ²-imidazolines, and Δ²-thiazolines (70).

(*ii*) 1,2-Difunctional ethanes (72, Z, Z′ = O, S, NH) react with carbonyl chloride and carbonate esters to give 2-oxazolidinones and analogous derivatives (72 → 71).

(*iii*) 1,2-Difunctional ethanes (72, Z, Z′ = O, S, NH) react with aldehydes and ketones to form oxazolidines, etc. (72 → 73). Such reactions are used extensively to protect *cis* hydroxyl groups (e.g. sugars + acetone → isopropylidine sugars) and carbonyl groups (e.g. steroidal ketones + ethylene glycol → ethylene ketals).

(*iv*) α-Acylamino-carboxylic acids are converted into 5(4*H*)-oxazolinones by acid anhydrides (74 → 75). In an extension of this reaction, N-acyl derivatives of glycine (74, R = H) react with aldehydes with concomitant cyclization to give azlactones (74 → 75 → 76); this is the basic Erlenmeyer synthesis of amino-acids.

$$\underset{69}{\overset{\displaystyle \text{CH}_2\text{NH}}{\underset{\displaystyle \text{CH}_2\text{ZH}}{\overset{\diagdown\text{COR}}{|\qquad}}}} \qquad \underset{70}{\boxed{}_Z}^N R \qquad \underset{71}{\boxed{}_Z}^{Z'}{}_O \overset{\text{COCl}_2 \text{ or}}{\underset{\text{CO(OEt)}_2}{\longleftarrow}} \underset{72}{\overset{\displaystyle \text{CH}_2\text{Z}'\text{H}}{\underset{\displaystyle \text{CH}_2\text{ZH}}{|\qquad}}} \overset{\text{O=CR}_2}{\longrightarrow} \underset{73}{\boxed{}_Z}^{Z'}{}^R_R$$

$$\underset{74}{\overset{\displaystyle \text{R}_2\text{C-NH}}{\underset{\displaystyle \text{HO}_2\text{C}\quad\text{COR}}{|\qquad|}}} \longrightarrow \underset{75}{\overset{R}{\underset{O}{\boxed{}_O}}N}R \longrightarrow \underset{76}{\overset{\overset{\displaystyle \text{H}}{\overset{|}{\text{RC}}}}{\underset{O}{\boxed{}_O}}N}R$$

3. Benzo Derivatives

(*i*) *o*-Hydroxy-, *o*-mercapto-, and *o*-amino-anilides (78, Z = O, S, NH) cyclize under mild conditions (e.g. heating at 150°, or refluxing with H₂O–HCl) to benzoxazoles, benzothiazoles, and benzimidazoles (79, Z = O, S, NH), respectively. The anilides are often prepared and cyclized *in situ* by heating the corresponding *o*-substituted anilines (77, Z = O, S, NH) with a carboxylic acid, anhydride, acid chloride, ester, nitrile, amidine, etc.

(*ii*) Benzoxazolones, benzothiazolones, and benzimidazolones are prepared by the reaction of carbonic acid derivatives with the corresponding *o*-substituted anilines.

(*iii*) If an aldehyde, ketone, or *gem*-dihalogeno compound is used in place of the carbonic acid derivative, the corresponding non-aromatic compound is formed (80 → 81).

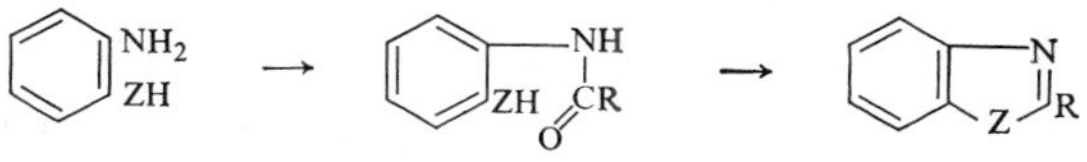

77   78   79

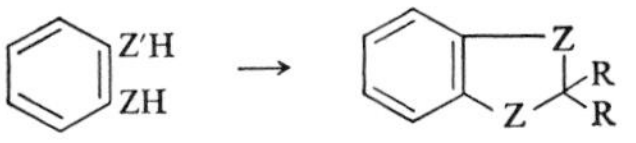

80   81

C. COMPOUNDS CONTAINING THREE OR MORE HETEROATOMS

1. Heteroatoms in the 1,2,3-Positions

(*i*) Acetylenes react with alkyl and aryl azides to give 1,2,3-triazoles (82 → 83). Olefins which are activated by electron-withdrawing groups, or are strained, similarly give 1,2,3-triazolines (84).

(*ii*) Diazoketones are converted by amines into 1,2,3-triazoles and by hydrogen sulphide into 1,2,3-thiadiazoles (85 → 86, Z = NR, S).

(*iii*) α-Dioximes (88) can be cyclized to furazans (87) and furoxans (89).

(*iv*) *o*-Phenylenediamine (91) is readily converted into benzo derivatives of 1,2,3-triazole (90) and 1,2,5-thiadiazole (92).

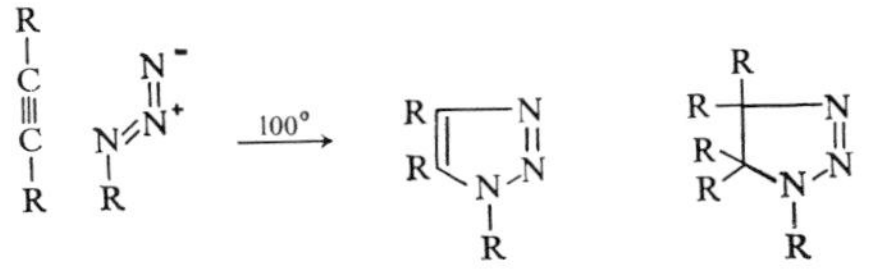

82   83   84

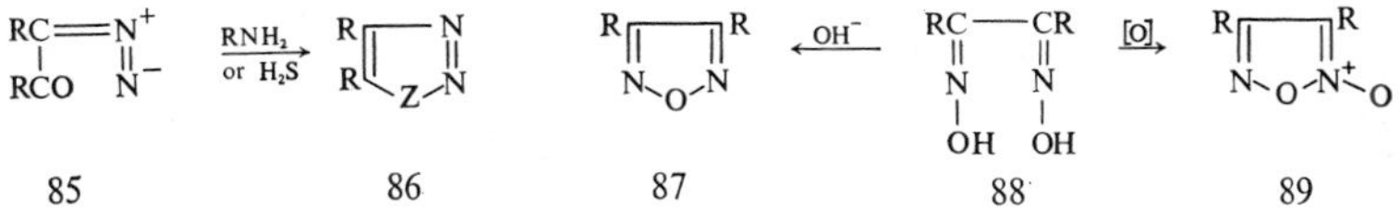

85   86   87   88   89

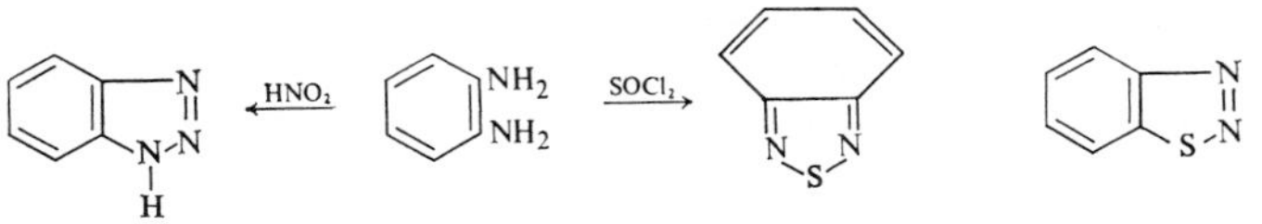

90   91   92.   93

(*v*) *o*-Mercaptoaniline and nitrous acid form benzo-1,2,3-thiadiaz-ole (93).

2. Heteroatoms in the 1,2,4-Positions

(*i*) Amidoximes and amidrazones (94, Z = O, NH) react with acid chlorides, etc. to give 1,2,4-oxadiazoles and 1,2,4-triazoles (95, Z = O, NH).

(*ii*) Diacyl-hydrazines (96) yield 1,3,4-oxadiazoles (97, Z = O) on heating or on treatment with $SOCl_2$, 1,3,4-thiadiazoles (97, Z = S) with P_2S_5, and 1,2,4-triazoles (97, Z = NR′) with primary amines.

(*iii*) Ozonides (98) result from the action of ozone on olefins.

94   95   96   97

98   99   100   101

3. Four or Five Heteroatoms

Tetrazoles (100) are formed by the action of nitrous acid on amidra-zones (99), and pentazoles (101) from the reaction of diazonium cations with azide anions.

III. REACTIONS OF THE AROMATIC RINGS

A. GENERAL SURVEY

1. Comparison with other Heterocycles

Replacing a CH group of benzene with a nitrogen atom gives pyridine (102); replacing a CH=CH group of benzene with NH, O, or S gives pyrrole, furan, or thiophene (104), respectively. The azoles (105 and 106) may be considered to be derived from benzene by two successive steps, one step of each of these types. The chemistry of five-membered aromatic rings with two or more heteroatoms shows

102   103   104   105   106   107

similarities to that of both the five- and the six-membered aromatic rings containing one heteroatom. Thus, electrophilic reagents attack lone electron pairs on multiply bonded nitrogen atoms of azoles (cf. pyridine), but they do not attack electron pairs on nitrogen atoms in NH groups or on O or S atoms (cf. pyrrole, furan, thiophene). The carbon atoms of azole rings can be attacked by nucleophilic, electrophilic, and free radical reagents. The thiazole, imidazole, and pyrazole nuclei show a high degree of aromatic character and usually 'revert to type' if the aromatic sextet is involved in a reaction; the isoxazole and oxazole nuclei are less aromatic. The reactions of cationic five-membered rings containing two heteroatoms (107, Z, Z′ = NR, O, S) are similar to those of pyridinium, pyrylium, and thiopyrylium cations.

108   109   110   111

2. Tautomerism

All triazoles and tetrazoles and unsymmetrically substituted imidazoles and pyrazoles can exist in two tautomeric forms (e.g. 108 ⇌ 109; 110 ⇌ 111). However, interconversion occurs readily (as discussed in Section 5.III.B.1), and such tautomers cannot be separated. Sometimes one tautomeric form predominates. Thus, the mesomerism of the benzene ring is greater in (108) than in (109), and ultraviolet spectral data show that benzotriazole exists predominantly as (108).

Hydroxy, amino, and mercapto derivatives of azoles are potentially tautomeric with alternative structures, some of which are comparable with the pyridones, etc., and others of which are comparable with the non-aromatic oxo-dihydropyrroles, etc.; this tautomerism is discussed in Sections 5.IV.4 and 5.

B. ELECTROPHILIC ATTACK AT A MULTIPLY-BONDED RING NITROGEN ATOM

1. Reaction Sequence

In azoles containing two annular nitrogen atoms one of which is an NH group and the other a multiply-bonded nitrogen atom, electrophilic attack occurs at the latter nitrogen and is usually followed by proton loss from the NH group (e.g. 112 → 114). If the electrophilic reagent is a proton, this reaction sequence leads to isomerization (cf. Section 5.III.A.2).

112   113   114   115   116

Since the electrophilic reagent attacks the multiply-bonded nitrogen atom (as shown for 115 and 116), the orientation of the reaction is related to the tautomeric structure of the starting material. However, any conclusion from chemical reactivity can be misleading if the minor component were to react preferentially and then be continually replenished by isomerization of the major component.

117   118   119   120   or   121

In addition to reaction sequences of type (112 → 114), electrophilic reagents can attack at either one of the ring nitrogen atoms in the mesomeric anions formed by proton loss (e.g. 117 → 120 or 121; cf. Section **5.III.D**.*e*).

2. Proton Acids

Mesomeric shifts of types (122) and (123) increase the electron density on the nitrogen atom and facilitate reaction with electrophilic reagents. However, the heteroatom Z also has an adverse inductive

122   123   124

effect; cf. the pK_a values of NH_2OH (6·0) and N_2H_4 (8·0), both of which are lower than that of NH_3 (9·5).

When both heteroatoms are nitrogen, the mesomeric effect predominates if they are in the 1,3-positions and the inductive effect if they are in the 1,2-positions. The predominance of the mesomeric effect is illustrated by the pK_a value of imidazole (122, Z = NH), which is 7·0, whereas that of pyrazole (123, Z = NH) is 2·5; cf. pyridine 5·2. When the second heteroatom is oxygen or sulphur the inductive, base-weakening effect increases; the pK_a of thiazole (122, Z = S) is 3·5 and that of isoxazole (123, Z = O) is 1·3.

Substituents alter the electron density at the multiply-bonded nitrogen atom, and therefore the basicity, just as in the pyridine series (see Section **2.III.B.1**.*b* for a discussion of this effect). The additional ring nitrogen atoms in triazoles, oxadiazoles, etc. are base weakening. This again is as expected since diazines are weaker bases than pyridine (see Section 3.III.2).

Annular nitrogen atoms can form hydrogen bonds, and if the azole contains an NH group, association occurs. Imidazole (124) shows a cryoscopic molecular weight in benzene twenty times that expected. Its boiling point is 256°, which is higher than that of 1-methylimidazole (198°).

3. Alkyl and Acyl Halides and Related Compounds

(*i*) Pyrazoles and imidazoles are readily alkylated (e.g. by MeI or Me_2SO_4); cf. reaction sequences (112 → 114) and (117 → 120 or 121). Unsymmetrical compounds usually give a mixture of products, the composition of which may depend on the reaction conditions. Thus, the ethoxycarbonylpyrazole (126) gives predominantly the isomeric N-methyl derivatives (125) and (127) under the conditions indicated. The difference in orientation can be related to the stabilization of the tautomeric structure (126) by hydrogen-bonding, which means that alkylation of the free base gives (127). The isomer (125) is formed *via* the anion.

(*ii*) Pyrazoles and imidazoles carrying a substituent on nitrogen, oxazoles, thiazoles, etc. are converted by alkyl halides into quaternary salts. This may be illustrated by the preparation of thiamine (130) from components (128) and (129).

(*iii*) N-Acyl-pyrazoles, -imidazoles, etc. can be prepared by reaction sequences of either type (112 → 114) or type (117 → 120, 121).

When two isomeric products could result, only the thermodynamically stable one is usually obtained because they interconvert easily. Thus, benzotriazole forms 1-acyl derivatives (131) which preserve the 'Kekulé resonance' of the benzene ring and are therefore more stable than the isomeric 2-derivatives.

C. ELECTROPHILIC ATTACK AT A RING CARBON ATOM

1. Reactivity and Orientation

(*a*) *Ease of Reaction.* Replacing a CH=CH group in benzene with a heteroatom, Z, increases the susceptibility of the ring carbon atoms to electrophilic attack noticeably when Z is S, and very markedly when Z is O or NH (cf. Section **4.III.B.1**). Replacing one CH group in benzene with a nitrogen atom decreases the ease of electrophilic attack at the remaining carbon atoms (cf. Section **2.III.A.1**); replacement of two CH groups with nitrogen atoms decreases it further (cf. Section **3.III.1**). This deactivation is pronounced in nitration, sulphonation, and Friedel-Crafts reactions which proceed in strongly acid media, i.e. under conditions in which the nitrogen atom is largely protonated (or complexed). For reactions conducted under neutral conditions, i.e. halogenation, mercuration, etc., the deactivating effect is less apparent.

The total effect of several heteroatoms in one ring approximates the superposition of their separate effects. Pyrazole, imidazole, oxazole, and isoxazole should therefore undergo nitration and sulphonation about as readily as benzene; thiazole and isothiazole should react less readily, and oxadiazoles, thiadiazoles, triazoles, etc. with still more difficulty. In each case, halogenation should be easier than the corresponding nitration or sulphonation. In general, these predictions are supported by available data.

Pyrazoles and imidazoles exist partly as anions (cf. 132 and 133) in neutral and basic solution and under these conditions react with electrophilic reagents about as readily as phenol; cf. the increased reactivity of pyrrole anions (Sections **4.III.C.1.***b* and *c*).

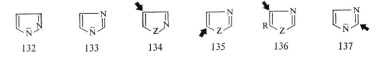

132   133   134   135   136   137

(*b*) *Orientation.* A multiply-bonded nitrogen atom deactivates carbon atoms α or γ to it towards electrophilic attack; thus, initial substitution in 1,2- and 1,3-dihetero compounds should be as shown

(134 and 135). Pyrazoles (134, Z = NH), isoxazoles (134, Z = O), imidazoles (135, Z = NH, tautomerism can make the 4- and 5-positions equivalent), and thiazoles (135, Z = S) do indeed undergo electrophilic substitution as predicted. Little is known of the electrophilic substitution reactions of isothiazoles (134, Z = S), oxazoles (135, Z = O), and compounds containing three or more heteroatoms in one ring. Deactivation of the 4-position in 1,3-dihetero compounds is less effective because of partial double bond fixation (cf. Sections **2.IV.A.1c** and **5.IV.1**), and if the 5-position is blocked, substitution takes place in the 4-position (136).

The above considerations do not apply to reactions of electrophilic reagents with pyrazole and imidazole anions (132, 133). The imidazole anion is substituted in the 2-position (137) and the indazole anion in the 3-position (Section **5.III.C.3**).

(c) Effect of Substituents. Just as in benzene, substituents can strongly activate (e.g. NH_2, NMe_2, OMe), strongly deactivate (e.g. NO_2, SO_3H, CO_2Et), or have relatively little effect on (e.g. Me, Cl) the ring towards further substitution. Further electrophilic substitution generally will not take place if the ring carries a strongly deactivating substituent. When the preferred substitution position (cf. 134 and 135) is occupied, strongly activating substituents can facilitate substitution in other positions (cf. Sections **5.III.C.2 and 3**).

2. Nitration, Sulphonation, and Halogenation

(*i*) Nitration and sulphonation of monocyclic compounds are summarized in the table. Substitution occurs in the expected positions. The conditions required are more vigorous than those for benzene, but less than those for pyridine.

Compound	Position substituted	Conditions for	
		Sulphonation	*Nitration*
Pyrazole	4($\equiv$5)	H_2SO_4–SO_3, 100°	HNO_3–H_2SO_4–SO_3,100°
Imidazole	4($\equiv$5)	H_2SO_4–SO_3, 160°	Boiling H_2SO_4–HNO_3
3-Methylisoxazole	4	HSO_3Cl, 100°	HNO_3–H_2SO_4–SO_3, 70°
4-Methylthiazole	5	H_2SO_4–SO_3, 200°	HNO_3–H_2SO_4–SO_3, 160°
2,5-Dimethylthiazole	4	H_2SO_4–SO_3, 200°	HNO_3–H_2SO_4–SO_3, 160°

The influence of activating groups is illustrated by the nitration (HNO_3–H_2SO_4 at *ca.* 20°) and sulphonation (H_2SO_4–SO_3 at *ca.* 100°) of (138) and (139).

(*ii*) Imidazoles and pyrazoles are easily chlorinated (Cl_2–H_2O or Cl_2–$CHCl_3$), brominated (Br_2–$CHCl_3$; $KOBr$–H_2O), and iodinated

138   139

(I_2–HIO_3). Generally initial substitution occurs at the 4-position, but further reaction at the other available nuclear positions takes place readily, especially in the imidazole series. When halogenation of the nucleus involves electrophilic attack on anions of type (132) and (133), the 2-position of imidazole is initially substituted.

3. Other Electrophiles

The wide variety of reactions with other electrophiles is illustrated by the following.

(*i*) Diazonium ions couple with imidazole and indazole (140) in the 2- and 3-positions, respectively; these reactions take place *via* the heterocyclic anions (e.g. 137 → 141). In general, the other azoles react only when they contain an amino, hydroxyl, or potential hydroxyl group; e.g. (142) and (143) react in the positions indicated.

140   141   142   143

144   145   146

(*ii*) Aldehydes and ketones react with azolinones. The reaction between aldehydes and 2-phenyl-5-oxazolone (144, Y = H_2), formed *in situ* from $PhCONHCH_2CO_2H$ and Ac_2O, gives azlactones (144, Y = RCH).

(*iii*) The pyrazole, imidazole, thiazole, triazole, and tetrazole rings are generally stable to oxidation ($KMnO_4$, CrO_3, etc.). Isoxazoles are more susceptible (e.g. 145 → 146, benzil α-monoxime benzoate), and oxazoles are readily oxidized (e.g. by $KMnO_4$).

D. NUCLEOPHILIC ATTACK AT THE RING CARBON ATOMS

(*a*) *General.* Because of the increased importance of inductive electron withdrawal, nucleophilic attack on uncharged azole rings occurs under conditions milder than those required for pyridines, pyridones, pyrones, and thiopyrones. Azolium rings are very easily attacked by nucleophilic reagents. Reactions similar to those of pyridinium and pyrylium compounds are shown; however, ring fission of azolium rings occurs still more readily.

(*b*) *Hydroxide and Alkoxide Ions.* These ions readily attack cationic rings; the initially formed pseudo-base can:

(*i*) Lose water to give an ether (e.g. 147 → 148), or

(*ii*) Be extensively degraded (e.g. 1,2-dimethylpyrazolium ion yields HCO_2H and $N_2H_2Me_2$).

Certain non-cationic rings can be opened by hydrolysis:

(*i*) Oxazoles are resistant to alkali but give acylamino-ketones (149) under acid conditions.

(*ii*) Isoxazoles unsubstituted in the 3-position react with hydroxide or ethoxide ions to give β-keto-nitriles (150 → 151).

(*iii*) Isoxazoles substituted in the 3-position, but unsubstituted in the 5-position, react under more vigorous conditions to give acids and nitriles (152 → 153).

(*iv*) Imidazoles and benzimidazoles (154) with acid chloride and alkali give compounds of type (156), probably *via* (155). 1,2,4-Triazoles and tetrazoles react similarly.

(*c*) *Amines.* Thiazoles can be aminated in the 2-position (by $NaNH_2$ at 150°).

Oxygen-containing rings can often be opened and reclosed to form a new heterocycle.

(*i*) Isoxazoles containing electron-withdrawing substituents give pyrazoles with hydrazine (e.g., 157, Z = O $\rightarrow$ 157, Z = NH).

(*ii*) Oxazoles give imidazoles with ammonia.

$$\underset{157}{Ph \overset{CO_2H}{\underset{Z-N}{\bigsqcup}}} \qquad \underset{158}{Me \overset{Me}{\underset{O-N}{\bigsqcup}}} \rightarrow \underset{159}{\overset{CH=CMe}{\underset{MeCO \quad NH_2}{\big|\qquad\big|}}}$$

(*d*) *Reducing Agents*

(*i*) Pyrazoles are reduced (Na–EtOH, H_2/Pd, etc.) to Δ^2-pyrazolines or pyrazolidines.

(*ii*) Imidazoles are generally resistant to reduction.

(*iii*) Isoxazoles are readily reduced, usually with concomitant ring fission (e.g. 158 $\rightarrow$ 159).

(*iv*) Oxazoles are reduced by sodium and ethanol to oxazolidines.

(*e*) *Deprotonation.* Thiazoles and 1-substituted imidazoles can be metallated in the 2-position (e.g. 160 $\rightarrow$ 161). Hydrogen atoms in the 2-position of thiazolium ions can be removed easily as protons (162 $\rightarrow$ 163); exchange with deuterium occurs in heavy water. This reaction has recently been extended to a wide range of other azolium cations.

$$\underset{160}{Me \overset{N}{\underset{Me \quad S}{\bigsqcup}}} \xrightarrow{PhLi} \underset{161}{Me \overset{N}{\underset{Me \quad S \quad Li}{\bigsqcup}}} \qquad \underset{162}{Me \overset{\overset{+}{N}-Me}{\underset{H \quad S \quad H}{\bigsqcup}}} \rightleftharpoons \underset{163}{Me \overset{\overset{+}{N}-Me}{\underset{H \quad S \quad -}{\bigsqcup}}}$$

E. OTHER REACTIONS OF THE AROMATIC NUCLEI

(*a*) *Nucleophilic Attack on the Ring NH Groups.* Pyrazoles, imidazoles, triazoles, and tetrazoles behave as weak acids. They form metallic salts (e.g. with $NaNH_2$, RMgBr) which are extensively hydrolyzed by water. The resulting anions react very readily with electrophilic reagents on either ring nitrogen or carbon atoms as discussed in Section 5.III.B.1.

(*b*) *Loss of Nitrogen.* Ring fission with loss of nitrogen occurs with azoles containing several nitrogen atoms.

(*i*) Pentazoles (164) spontaneously form azides, usually below 20°.

164 165 166

167 168

(*ii*) Tetrazoles with acid chlorides (in C_5H_5N at 50°) give 1,3,4-oxadiazoles [e.g. (165) with PhCOCl yields (166)].

(*iii*) 1-Phenylbenzotriazoles form carbazoles (167 → 168).

IV. REACTIONS OF SUBSTITUENTS ON AROMATIC NUCLEI

1. General Survey

(*a*) *Heteroatoms in the 1,3-Positions.* The 2-position in imidazoles, thiazoles, and oxazoles is electron deficient, and substituents in the 2-position (169) generally show the same reactions as α- or γ-substituents on pyridines.

(*i*) 2-Halogens are relatively easily replaced.

(*ii*) 2-Methyl groups are active.

(*iii*) 2-Hydroxyl compounds exist in the azolinone form.

Substituents in the 4-position of these compounds are also α to a multiply-bonded nitrogen atom, but, because of bond fixation, they are little influenced by this nitrogen atom even when it is quaternized (170). This should be compared with 3-substituents on isoquinolines

169 170 171 172

(cf. Section 2.IV.A.1.*c*). In general, substituents in the 4- and 5-positions of imidazoles, thiazoles, and oxazoles show the reactions of the same substituents on benzenoid compounds.

(*b*) *Heteroatoms in the 1,2-Positions.* Substituents on pyrazoles and isoxazoles, regardless of their positions, generally show the reactions of the same substituent on a benzene ring rather than those of α- or γ-substituents on pyridine. The (electron-releasing) mesomeric effect of the 'pyrrole-type' NH group and 'furan-type' O atom is evidently more important than their (electron-withdrawing) inductive effect in pyrazole and isoxazole. However, halogen atoms and methyl groups in the 3- and 5-positions of pyrazoles and isoxazoles (171) are 'active' if the ring is quaternized (172).

2. Carbon-Containing Substituents

(*a*) *Fused Benzene Rings.* In benzazoles electrophilic substitution takes place in the benzenoid ring under conditions similar to those used for benzene itself. The actual position attacked varies (cf. formulae 173–177) for reasons which are not well understood.

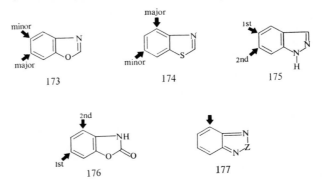

(*b*) *Aryl Groups.* Electrophilic substitution occurs readily in aryl groups, usually predominantly at the *p*-position. Thus, the nitration of phenyl-thiazoles, -oxazoles, and -imidazoles (HNO_3–H_2SO_4 at 100°) yields the corresponding *p*-nitrophenyl derivatives.

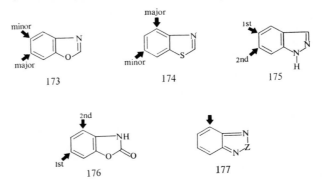

178	179	180	181

(*c*) *Alkyl Groups.* Methyl groups in the 2-position of imidazoles, oxazoles, and thiazoles (178, Z = NH, O, S) are 'active'; i.e., they can lose protons and give anions which react with electrophilic reagents in a manner similar to those from α- and γ-methylpyridines. Thus, methyl compounds of type (178) with $ZnCl_2$ and PhCHO yield styryl derivatives (179).

   In the cationic derivatives (e.g. 180), methyl groups in the 2-position are still more reactive, and proton loss is facilitated. The resulting anhydro-bases (181) can be isolated or allowed to react *in situ*. These reactions parallel those of the corresponding pyridinium compounds (Section **2.IV.A.3**).

In general, methyl groups in the 4- and 5-positions of imidazole, oxazole, and thiazole do not undergo such reactions, even when the ring is cationic. Methyl groups on pyrazoles and isoxazoles are also relatively unreactive.

Alkyl groups can usually be oxidized to carboxyl groups without disruption of the nucleus (e.g. by $KMnO_4$).

(*d*) *Acyl Groups*. N-Acyl-azoles are readily hydrolyzed. Their susceptibility to nucleophilic attack has led to compounds such as carbonyl-bis-imidazole (182) which have synthetic utility, e.g. in peptide syntheses.

3. Halogens

Halogen atoms in the 2-position of imidazoles, thiazoles, and oxazoles (183) undergo nucleophilic substitution reactions. The conditions required are more vigorous than those used for α- or γ-halogenopyridines (Section **2.IV.A.5**) but much less severe than those required for chlorobenzene. Thus, in compounds of type (183, X = Cl, Br), the halogen atom can be replaced by the groups NHR, OR, SH, and OH (in the last two instances, the products tautomerize; see Section 5.IV.4).

Halogen atoms in the 4- and 5-positions of imidazoles, thiazoles, and oxazoles and those in pyrazoles and isoxazoles, do not normally show this reactivity unless they are labilized by an α- or γ-electron-withdrawing substituent.

Nuclear halogen atoms can be replaced with hydrogen atoms by chemical or catalytic reduction (e.g. Na–EtOH, Zn–HOAc, and H_2–Ni). Derived Grignard reagents, which show the normal reactions, are usually prepared by the 'entrainment method' (cf. Section **2.IV.A.5**).

4. Potential Hydroxy Compounds

(*a*) *2-Hydroxy, Heteroatoms-1,3*. 2-Hydroxy-imidazoles, -oxazoles, and -thiazoles (184, Z = NR, O, S) can isomerize to 2-azolinones (185). These compounds all exist predominantly in the azolinone form and show reactions similar to those of the pyridones (see Section **2.IV.A.6.***d*).

(*i*) They are converted by $POCl_3$ at 100–200° into chloro-azoles (e.g. 185 → 186).

(*ii*) Alkylation gives C–, O–, or N–alkyl derivatives [e.g. (188) forms (187) or (189)].

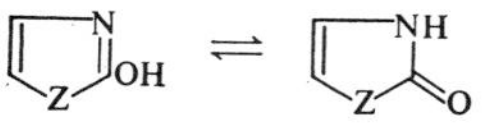

184   ⇌   185

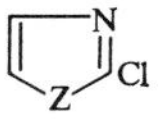

186 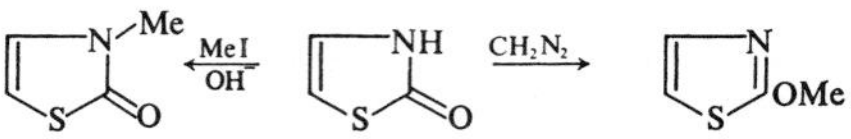   187   MeI / OH⁻ ← → 188   CH₂N₂ →   189

(*b*) *3-Hydroxy, Heteroatoms-1,2.* Pyrazoles, isoxazoles, and isothiazoles with a hydroxyl group in the 3-position (190, Z = NR, O, S) could isomerize to 3-azolinones (191). However, these compounds behave as true hydroxy derivatives and show phenolic properties.

(*c*) *4- and 5-Hydroxy, Heteroatoms-1,3 and 4-Hydroxy, Heteroatoms-1,2.* 4- and 5-Hydroxy-imidazoles, -oxazoles, and -thiazoles (192, 194) and 4-hydroxy-pyrazoles, -isoxazoles, and -isothiazoles (196) cannot tautomerize to an aromatic carbonyl form. However, tautomerism similar to that which occurs in hydroxy-furans, -thiophenes, and -pyrroles is possible (192 ⇌ 193; 194 ⇌ 195; 196 ⇌ 197). Most compounds of this type exist largely in these non-aromatic azolinone forms (193, 195, 197). However, the hydroxyl form can be stabilized by chelation (e.g. 198).

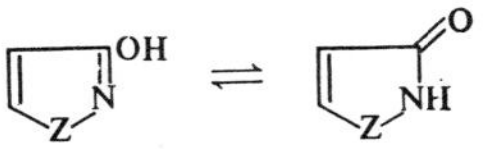

190   ⇌   191

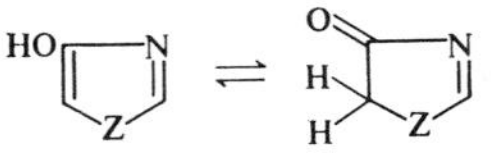

192   ⇌   193 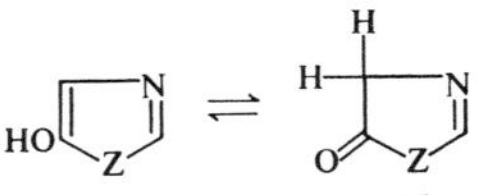   194   ⇌   195

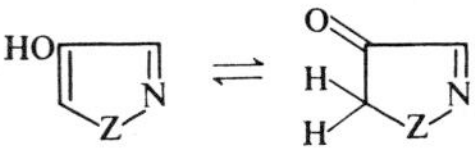

196   ⇌   197 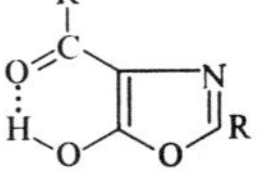   198

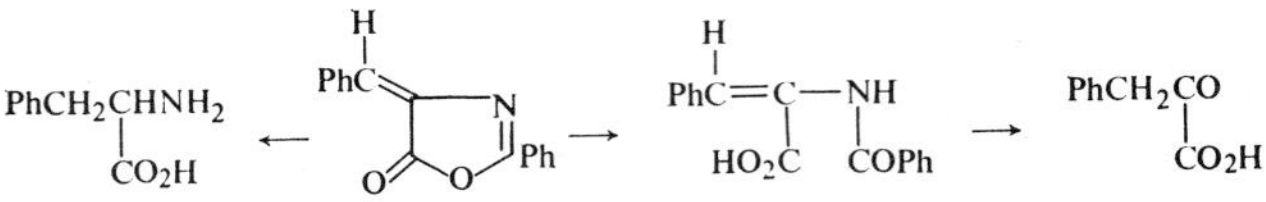

199   ←   200   →   201   →   202

Ring fission occurs readily in most of these compounds. For example, azlactones, i.e. 5(4*H*)-oxazolones, containing an exocyclic C=C bond at the 4-position (200) are hydrolyzed to α-benzamido α,β-unsaturated acids (201), further hydrolysis of which gives α-keto-acids (202). Reduction and subsequent hydrolysis *in situ* of azlactones is used in the synthesis of α-amino-acids (e.g. 200 → 199).

(*d*) *5-Hydroxy, Heteroatoms-1,2.* 5-Hydroxy-isoxazoles and -pyra-zoles can tautomerize in both of the ways discussed in (*a*) and (*c*) above (203 ⇌ 204 ⇌ 205). The hydroxy form is generally the least stable; the alternative azolinone forms coexist in proportions de-pending on the substituents and the solvent.

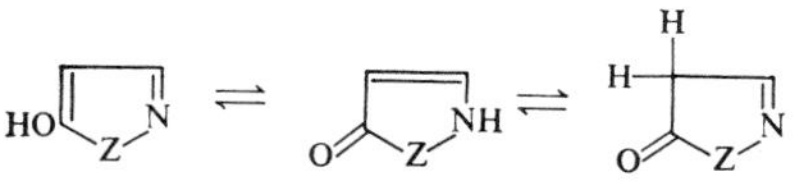

203   204   205

5. Amino Groups

Amino-azoles exist predominantly as such and not in the tautomeric imino forms. They resemble aminopyridines (cf. Section 2.IV.A.7.*b*) in many ways:

(*i*) The basicity of these amino groups is lower than that in aniline, and protons add preferentially to the annular nitrogen atoms.

(*ii*) Alkylation takes place on a ring nitrogen atom, except under conditions where an intermediate anion is the reactive species (cf. 207 → 206, 209).

(*iii*) Acylation gives acylamino derivatives.

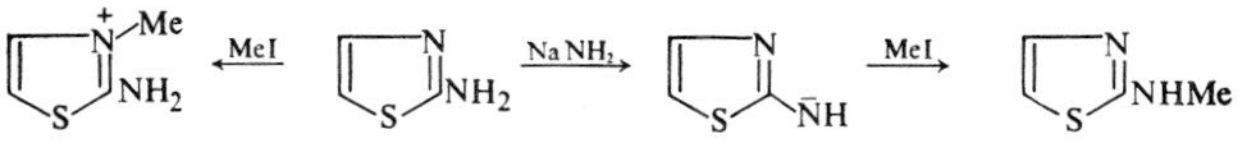

206   207   208   209

Amino-azoles can usually be diazotized more readily than α- or γ-aminopyridine, although a strongly acidic medium is often required. The resulting diazo compounds undergo many of the normal coupling and displacement reactions.

V. REACTIONS OF NON-AROMATIC COMPOUNDS

Non-aromatic derivatives of the azoles generally react similarly to their aliphatic analogues; the principal exceptions involve aroma-tization.

(*a*) *Dihydro Compounds.* Δ⁴-Imidazolines,-oxazolines,and -thiazolines
(210), and their benzo derivatives (213), are very easily aromatized
(213 → 214), and syntheses which might be expected to yield dihydro
compounds often afford the corresponding aromatic products.

Δ²-Imidazolines (211, Z = NH) are cyclic amidines and exhibit
the characteristic resonance stabilization and high basicity. Δ²-
Oxazolines (211, Z = O) are cyclic imino-ethers, and Δ²-thiazolines
(211, Z = S) are imino-thioethers; both are consequently easily
hydrolyzed by dilute acid.

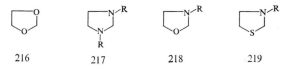

210   211   212   213   214   215

Δ²-Pyrazolines and Δ²-isoxazolines (212, Z = NH, O) are cyclic
hydrazones and oximes, respectively. Δ²-Pyrazolines are oxidized by
bromine or Pb(OAc)₄ to pyrazoles; they lose nitrogen on pyrolysis
to give cyclopropanes (e.g. 212, Z = NH → 215).

(*b*) *Tetrahydro Compounds.* 1,3-Dioxolanes (216), tetrahydroimida-
zoles (217), tetrahydro-oxazoles (218), and tetrahydrothiazoles (219)
are somewhat more easily formed than their acyclic analogues, but
their properties are otherwise similar. Compounds of types (217,
R = H) and (218, R = H) are in equilibrium with their open-chain
forms. These tetrahydro compounds are readily hydrolyzed by dilute
acid.

216   217   218   219

(*c*) *Non-Aromatic Derivatives of Azolinones.* These compounds are
considered in Section 5.IV.4.

CHAPTER SIX

Heterocyclic Compounds with Three- and Four-Membered Rings

I. THREE-MEMBERED RINGS

A. THREE-MEMBERED RINGS WITH ONE HETEROATOM

1. Nomenclature and Compounds
The parent compounds are:
  (*i*) Aziridine (or ethylenimine) (1, Z = NH),
  (*ii*) Oxirane (or ethylene oxide) (1, Z = O), and
  (*iii*) Thiirane (or ethylene sulphide) (1, Z = S).

1	2	3	4

Derivatives with a carbonyl group or double bond in the ring have been postulated as reaction intermediates, but it is only recently that an α-lactam (2) and an azirine (3) have been isolated.

2. Preparation
These compounds can be prepared by nucleophilic displacement reactions.

  (*i*) Oxiranes are formed by the action of alkali on β-hydroxy-halides (4, Y = Br, Cl), β-hydroxy-tosylates (4, Y = TsO), and β-hydroxy-quaternary ammonium ions (4, Y = NMe_3^+). They are also formed as by-products in the reaction of diazoalkanes with ketones (e.g. 5 → 8).

5	6	7	8

(*ii*) Thiiranes are prepared by similar methods, i.e. alkali plus β-mercapto-halides (9), and by the reaction of diazomethane with thioketones (cf. 5). The most important method for the preparation of thiiranes is the reaction of thiourea with oxiranes; it involves ring opening and subsequent closure.

9   10

(*iii*) β-Amino-halides and β-amino-sulphates (10, Y = Br, Cl, SO$_4^-$) give aziridines on heating or on treatment with alkali.

In addition to these preparative methods involving nucleophilic displacement, oxiranes are formed by direct oxidation of olefins with oxygen (catalytic) or peracids (e.g. PhCO$_3$H–CHCl$_3$ at 20°). This reaction is facilitated by alkylation of the C=C bond of the olefin and hindered by the presence of electron-withdrawing groups.

3. Reactions

These three-membered ring compounds, because of ring strain, are much more reactive than normal ethers, sulphides, and amines. Nucleophilic reagents open the ring (11 → 12) *via* reactions which are the reverse of the preparative methods; electrophiles can catalyze these reactions, for ring fission of (13) is easier than that of (11). Under basic or neutral conditions ring fission takes place preferentially at the least substituted carbon and is accompanied by inversion (i.e. S$_N$2 type); under acid conditions these rules do not always apply because of increasing S$_N$1 character.

The reactions of these heterocyclic systems include those initiated by the following reagents:

(*i*) Hydroxide ions: oxiranes → glycols, aziridines → amino-alcohols.

(*ii*) Amines: oxiranes → amino-alcohols, aziridines → diamines.

(*iii*) Hydrogen halides: oxiranes → halohydrins, thiiranes → mercapto-halides, aziridines → halogeno-amines.

11   12   13   14

(*iv*) Grignard reagents: oxiranes → alcohols (e.g. C_2H_4O + $RMgBr$ → $R-CH_2CH_2OH$).

(*v*) Catalytic amounts of either a nucleophilic or an electrophilic reagent can induce polymerization; ring fission occurs first, and the ring-fission product reacts with additional molecules of the cyclic starting material giving dimers (e.g. 14) or high polymers (e.g. $\cdots CH_2CH_2-Z-CH_2CH_2-Z-CH_2\ CH_2 \cdots$).

(*vi*) Reducing agents (e.g. $Ni-H_2$, $Zn-NH_4Cl$, P–I, Al–Hg). Oxiranes and aziridines are reduced to alcohols and amines, respectively.

(*vii*) Electrophiles ($MgBr_2$; H_2SO_4–AcOH) catalyze the rearrangement of oxiranes to ketones; the migration aptitudes of the various substituents parallel those for the related pinacol–pinacolone rearrangement.

(*viii*) Aziridines can be acylated and nitrosated on the nitrogen atom. They form salts with acids but are less basic (pK_a *ca.* 8) than normal secondary amines (pK_a *ca.* 11).

B. THREE-MEMBERED RINGS CONTAINING TWO HETEROATOMS

(*i*) Oxaziridines (15) are formed by oxidation ($MeCO_3H-CH_2Cl_2$ at 20°) of Schiff's bases. They are rearranged by heat to nitrones (16) and/or amides (17).

$$\overset{15}{}\qquad \overset{+}{R_2C=NR}\underset{O^-}{} \quad 16 \qquad R-\underset{\underset{O}{\|}}{C}-NR_2 \quad 17$$

(*ii*) Diaziridines (18) are prepared by the reaction R_2CO + $R'NH_2$ + NH_2OSO_3H → (18). Diaziridines are weak bases and can be acylated on the nitrogen atom. The ring is easily broken, e.g. by reducing agents.

18   19

(*iii*) Diazirines (19) are produced by the oxidation of N-unsubstituted diaziridines: (18, R' = H) + Ag_2O → (19). The diazirines are isomers of the aliphatic diazo compounds, but are much less reactive than diazo compounds, although they resemble them in being explosive. Grignard reagents yield N-substituted diaziridines.

II. FOUR-MEMBERED RINGS

A. FOUR-MEMBERED RINGS CONTAINING ONE HETEROATOM

1. Nomenclature and Compounds

The parent compounds comprise:

(*i*) Azetidine (or trimethylenimine) (20, Z = NH),
(*ii*) Oxetane (or trimethylene oxide) (20, Z = O), and
(*iii*) Thietane (or trimethylene sulphide) (20, Z = S).

Their α-carbonyl derivatives (21) are named systematically as 2-azetidinone, etc., but the β-lactam, β-lactone, and β-thiolactone nomenclature is also frequently used.

The penicillins (22, R = CH_2Ph, etc.), which contain a β-lactam ring, are important antibiotics.

20 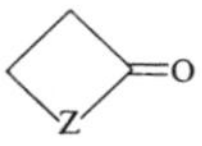   21 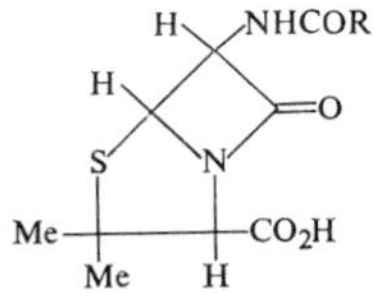   22 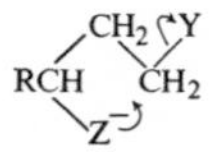   23

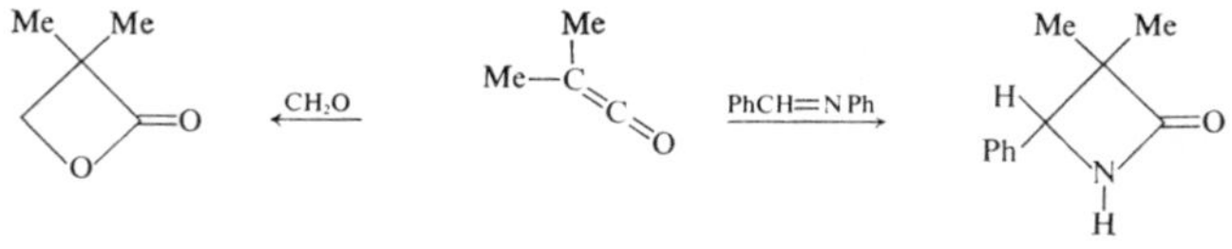

24   25   26

2. Preparation

Azetidines, oxetanes, and thietanes are prepared by nucleophilic displacement reactions (23), e.g. by the action of alkali on γ-halogeno-amines, -alcohols, and -mercaptans. These reactions are analogous to those employed for the synthesis of three-membered rings (Section 6.I.A.2); however, they proceed less smoothly.

2-Oxetanones (β-lactones) and 2-azetidinones (β-lactams) are conveniently prepared from ketenes (25 → 24, 26). Synthetic methods involving ring closure are also known (e.g. $ICH_2CH_2CO_2Ag$ → 2-oxetanone).

3. Reactions

(*a*) *Saturated Rings.* The properties of azetidine, oxetane, and thietane are intermediate between those of aliphatic amines, ethers, and
sulphides on the one hand and those of the corresponding three-
membered ring systems on the other.

(*i*) In some reactions the ring is preserved. Thietane can be oxidized
to a sulphone. Azetidine forms salts and can be acylated (with
RCOCl) or nitrosated (with HNO_2).

(*ii*) Ring fission occurs readily. Oxetane reacts with Grignard
reagents to give alcohols of type $R(CH_2)_3OH$ and with hydrogen
bromide to give 1,3-dibromopropane. Hydrogen halides convert
azetidine into γ-halogeno-amines.

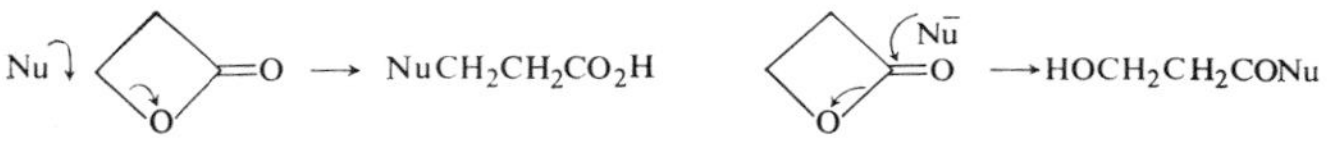

27   28   29   30

(*b*) *Carbonyl Derivatives.* 2-Oxetanones (β-lactones) are readily
attacked by nucleophilic reagents. Reaction can occur by:

(*i*) Alkyl-oxy fission ($27 \rightarrow 28$) [e.g. propiolactone with
$NaOAc-H_2O$ yields (28, Nu = Ac), with MeOH–NaOMe it forms
(28, Nu = OMe)].

(*ii*) Acyl-oxy fission ($29 \rightarrow 30$) [e.g. propiolactone reacts with
MeOH–H$^+$ to give (30, Nu = OMe)].

The reaction of 2-azetidinones (β-lactams) with nucleophilic
reagents is accompanied by acyl-nitrogen fission, as is normal for
amides (cf. $29 \rightarrow 30$); e.g., propiolactam yields β-alanine
($NH_2CH_2CH_2CO_2H$) on hydrolysis.

B. FOUR-MEMBERED RINGS CONTAINING TWO HETEROATOMS

Four-membered rings with heteroatoms in the 1,2-positions may be
prepared from ketenes:

(*i*) Azo compounds give 1,2-diazetidines (e.g. $32 \rightarrow 31$).

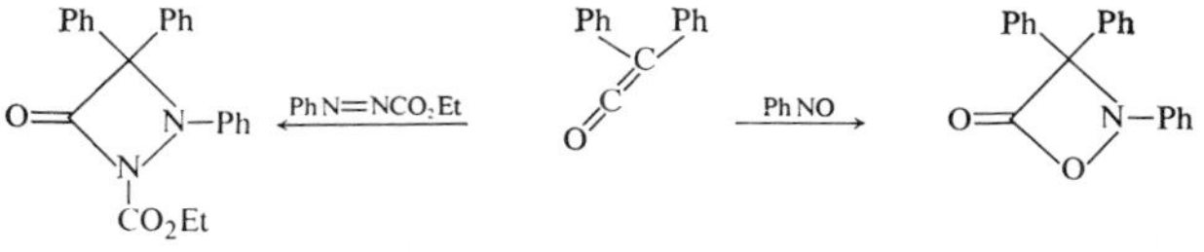

31   32   33

(*ii*) Nitroso compounds give 1,2-oxazetidines (e.g. 32 ⟶ 33).

1,3-Diazetidine derivatives can be prepared by condensation of isocyanates with Schiff's bases (e.g. 34 ⟶ 35).

34   35

CHAPTER SEVEN

Physical Properties

---

1. Melting Points and Boiling Points

The melting and boiling points for some heteroaromatic systems and their monosubstituted derivatives are collected in the table on page 166.

(*a*) *Unsubstituted Compounds.* A comparison between the boiling points of the parent ring systems (first column of table) shows that replacement of a —CH=CH— group with a sulphur atom has little effect, and that replacement of a —CH=CH— group with an oxygen atom lowers the boiling point by *ca.* 40°. These effects are to be expected on the basis of the decreased molecular weight.

The introduction of nitrogen atoms into the ring is accompanied by less regular changes. Substitution of either a —CH=CH— group by an NH group or of a =CH— group by a nitrogen atom increases the boiling point. If both of these changes are made simultaneously, the boiling point is increased by an especially large amount due to the possibilities of association by hydrogen bonding (cf. Section 5.III.B.2).

(*b*) *Effect of Substituents.* Examination of the effects of substituents on the melting and boiling points of the parent compounds is instructive.

(*i*) Methyl and ethyl groups attached to ring carbon atoms usually increase the boiling point by *ca.* 20–30° and *ca.* 50–60°, respectively. However, conversion of an NH group into an NR group results in large decreases in the boiling point (e.g. pyrazole → 1-methyl-pyrazole) because of decreased ease of association.

(*ii*) The acids and amides are all solids. Carboxy derivatives of compounds containing a ring nitrogen atom usually melt higher than those containing annular oxygen or sulphur atoms because the hydrogen bonding possibilities are increased. Nearly all the amides melt in the range 130–180°.

(*iii*) Compounds containing both a ring nitrogen atom and a hydroxyl, mercapto, or amino group are usually relatively high

165

MELTING AND BOILING POINTS [a,b,]

Ring system	H	Me	Et	COMe	CO₂H	CO₂Et	CONH₂	CN	NH₂	OH	OMe	SH	SMe	Cl	Br
Benzene	**80**	111	136	202	**122**	211	130	190	184	**43**	**37**	168	187	131	155
Pyridine-2	**115**	128	148	192	**137**	243	107	222	57	**107**	252	**128**	197	171	193
„ -3	„	144	163	220	**235**	223	129	**50**	65	**125**	179d	79	—	150	173
„ -4	„	145	171	211	**306**	219	156	79	**157**	**148**	93	**186**	—	147	174
Pyrrole-1	**130**	114	129	180	**95d**	180	166	—	—	—	—	—	—	—	—
„ -2	„	148	181	**90**	**205d**	39	174	—	—	—	—	—	**44**	—	—
„ -3	„	158	179	**115**	**148**	78d	152	—	—	—	—	—	—	—	—
Furan-2	**31**	64	92	**31**	**133**	34	142	147	68	80	110	—	—	78	103
„ -3	„	65	—	**54**	**122**	179	168	—	—	58	—	—	—	80	103
Thiophene-2	**84**	113	133	214	**129**	218	180	196	214	217	154	166	—	128	150
„ -3	„	115	135	**57**	**138**	208	178	179	—	—	—	171	—	136	157
Pyrazole-1	**70**	127	137	234	—	213	—	—	—	—	—	—	—	—	—
„ -4	„	207	—	157	**275**	**160**	—	—	—	—	—	—	—	**77**	**97**
„ -3	„	205	209	**101**	**214d**	—	134	—	—	—	—	—	—	—	—
Isoxazole-3	**95**	118	138	—	**149d**	218	134	168	**81**	**118**	—	—	—	—	—
„ -5	„	122	—	**53**	149	—	174	—	285	**164**	—	—	—	—	—
Imidazole-1	**90**	199	226	**102**	—	—	—	—	—	—	—	—	—	—	—
„ -2	„	141	**80**	**80**	**164d**	**157**	215	—	—	250d	—	227	139	—	207
„ -4	„	**56**	—	—	**275d**	—	—	—	—	—	—	—	—	—	130
Oxazole-2	**69**	87	—	—	—	—	—	—	97	—	—	—	—	—	—
„ -4	—	—	—	—	142	48	—	—	—	—	—	—	—	—	—
Thiazole-2	**117**	128	—	**56**	102d	48	—	—	90	—	—	79	—	145	147
„ -4	„	133	—	—	196	217	150	**53**	—	—	—	—	—	—	—
„ -5	„	154	—	—	218	68	186	—	—	—	—	—	—	—	—
Pyridazine-3	**208**	215	—	—	200	255	182	—	**83**	103	219	—	—	**35**	**73**
„ -4	„	225	—	—	240	—	191	—	169	—	—	—	—	—	—
Pyrimidine-2	**123**	138	—	—	270	—	—	—	127	320	—	230d	—	65	—
„ -4	„	141	—	—	240d	—	212	—	151	164	—	187	218	—	—
„ -5	„	153	—	—	270	—	—	—	170	210d	—	—	—	—	75
Pyrazine-2	**57**	135	—	—	229d	38	189	205	—	119	187	—	—	160	180

[a] Melting points above 30° are given in **bold**; melting points below 30° are not included.

[b] Boiling points are given at atmospheric pressure; those reported at other than atmospheric pressure were converted using a nomogram (*Ind. Eng. Chem.*, 1957, **49**, 125).

[c] A dash indicates that the compound is unstable, unknown, or the data are not readily available.

melting solids. For many hydroxyl and mercapto compounds, this can be attributed to their tautomerism with hydrogen-bonded 'one' and 'thione' forms (cf. Sections **2.IV.A**.6 and 8). However, hydrogen bonding can evidently also occur in hydroxyl compounds, e.g. 3-hydroxypyridine, and in amino compounds.

(*iv*) Methoxyl, methylthio, and dimethylamino derivatives are often liquids.

(*v*) Chloro compounds usually have boiling points similar to those of the corresponding ethyl compounds. Bromo compounds boil approximately 25° higher than their chloro analogues.

2. Refractive Indices, Specific Gravities, and Viscosities

The parent heterocyclic compounds and their lower homologues are mobile liquids with densities not very different from that of water and have moderately high refractive indices. The physical constants for a few heterocyclic compounds are compared with those for benzene in the following table.

Benzene	n_D^{20}	1·501	d_4^{20}	0·879	η^{20}	0·652
Pyridine	n_D^{21}	1·509	d_4^{25}	0·978	η^{20}	0·974
Pyrrole	n_D^{20}	1·508	d_4^{20}	0·969	–	
Furan	n_D^{19}	1·422	d_4^{20}	0·937	–	
Thiophene	n_D^{20}	1·525	d_4^{20}	1·062	η^{22}	0·638

3. Dipole Moments

The dipole moment gives a measure of the overall charge distribution in a molecule. By comparison with suitable standards, conclusions regarding the mesomerism of a system can be drawn. For example, it has been shown that:

(*i*) The annular nitrogen atom in pyrroles carries a partial positive charge (importance of canonical structures 1 and 2).

(*ii*) The ring heteroatoms in 4-pyrones and 4-thiopyrones act as electron donors (cf. canonical form 3).

(*iii*) The 4-position of the pyridine nucleus is electron deficient.

(*iv*) Electrons can be made available at, or withdrawn from, the 4-position of the pyridine 1-oxide nucleus depending on the electronic requirements of the substituents present (cf. Section **2.III.A**.4).

4. pK$_a$ Values

An acid, HA, tends to ionize according to the equation HA $\rightleftharpoons$ H$^+$ + A$^-$. The strength of the acid HA is defined by the expression $\dfrac{[H^+][A^-]}{[HA]} = K_a$, where K$_a$ is the dissociation constant. For convenience, pK$_a$ values are usually quoted; pK$_a$ $= -\log_{10}$ K$_a$. The strength of a base, B, is conveniently expressed in terms of its conjugate acid, BH$^+$: the stronger the conjugate acid, the weaker is the base. Thus, high pK$_a$ values indicate weak acids and the conjugate acids of strong bases, and low pK$_a$ values denote strong acids and the conjugate acids of weak bases.

The basicity of an annular nitrogen atom depends on the electron density at that atom; thus, variations in the electron density caused by changing the substituents can be measured by determining basicity changes. The pK$_a$ values of pyridines, azines, and azoles are discussed in this context in Sections 2.III.B.1, 3.III.2, and 5.III.B.2.

pK$_a$ VALUES OF POTENTIALLY TAUTOMERIC AND
REFERENCE COMPOUNDS

4-Benzylthiopyridine (4, R = CH$_2$Ph)	5·4	2-Dimethylaminopyridine 1-oxide (6, R = Me)	2·3
1-Methyl-4-pyridinethione (5, R = Me)	1·4	1-Methoxy-2-pyridonimine (7, R = Me)	12·4
4-Pyridinethione (5, R = H) *or* 4-mercaptopyridine (4, R = H)	1·5	2-Aminopyridine 1-oxide (6, R = H) *or* 1-hydroxy-2-pyridonimine (7, R = H)	2·7

Basicity measurements have been used extensively to determine the predominant structure of potentially tautomeric compounds. If pK$_a$ and pK$_a{}'$ are the values for the individual tautomeric forms, the equilibrium constant for the tautomerism can be obtained from the equation $-\log$ K$_T$ = pK$_a$ $-$ pK$_a{}'$. Alkylation does not greatly alter the pK$_a$ values, and, therefore, approximate values for tautomeric constants can be determined. Thus, for example, the pK$_a$ values tabulated above show that 4-pyridinethione (5, R = H) and 2-aminopyridine 1-oxide (6, R = H) are the predominant tautomeric forms existing in the equilibria (4 $\rightleftharpoons$ 5, R = H) and (6 $\rightleftharpoons$ 7, R = H) and that the tautomeric constants, K_T, are *ca.* 10^4 and 10^{10}, respectively.

5. Ultraviolet Spectra

The ultraviolet spectra of heterocyclic compounds containing aromatic five- and/or six-membered rings show an overall resemblance to the spectra of the corresponding aromatic benzenoid compounds (i.e. with the same number of fused aromatic rings). The effects of substituents on the spectra of heterocyclic compounds are generally similar to those observed in the benzenoid series.

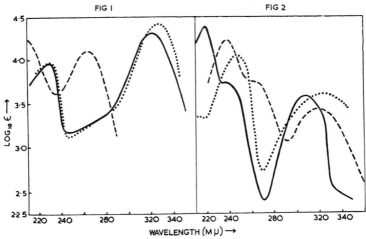

Fig. 1: ——— 4-Pyridinethione (5, R = H)
          ⋯⋯ 1-Methyl-4-pyridinethione (5, R = Me)
          - - - - 4-Benzylthiopyridine (4, R = CH₂Ph)

Fig. 2: ——— 2-Aminopyridine 1-oxide (6, R = H)
          ⋯⋯ 1-Methoxy-2-pyridonimine (7, R = Me)
          - - - - 2-Dimethylaminopyridine 1-oxide (6, R = Me)

Ultraviolet spectra have been used to investigate the structures of potentially tautomeric compounds. Figures 1 and 2 show the spectra of the compounds for which pK_a values are given in the preceding section; these spectra are further indication that the potentially tautomeric compounds exist as 4-pyridinethione and 2-aminopyridine 1-oxide. In principle, tautomeric constants may be determined from ultraviolet spectral data (because alkylation has little effect on these spectra), but in practice this can usually be done only if at least *ca.* 5% of each isomer is present in the equilibrium mixture.

6. Infrared Spectra

The infrared spectra of a heterocyclic compound, like that of any organic compound, provides an excellent fingerprint, and is far more characteristic than, e.g., the melting point.

Considerable progress has been made recently in the interpretation of the infrared spectra of heterocycles. For most vibrational modes of complex molecules, the movement is concentrated in a portion of the molecule, e.g. in an aromatic ring or in a substituent. Compounds containing the same substituent or the same aromatic ring show characteristic bands which can be used for diagnostic purposes.

The influence of the remainder of the molecule on the position and/or intensity of the bands can give information concerning the relative electron-donating and electron-withdrawing ability of aromatic nuclei at various positions. Thus, the double bond character of the $C=O$ bond in compounds such as $\overset{\frown}{Ar}-CR\overset{\frown}{=}O$ is determined by the electron-donating ability of the nucleus.

7. Nuclear Magnetic Resonance Spectra

Since they were first widely used by organic chemists, about 1955, nuclear magnetic resonance spectra, particularly proton resonance spectra, have rapidly increased in importance. They provide an excellent means of characterization for heterocyclic compounds, and the presence and nature of impurities can often be detected. The proportionality of peak areas to concentration of absorbing species allows application to quantitative analysis and to the determination of reaction kinetics.

Uses in structural elucidations are numerous. Chemical shifts depend on chemical environment, and relative areas give the numbers of each type of protons: aromatic, olefinic, aliphatic, aldehydic, etc. Spin-spin coupling constants supply information about the relative orientation of hydrogen atoms: they are particularly useful in conformational questions.

The 'ring current', which can be determined from chemical shifts, is widely used as a criterion of aromaticity.

N.m.r. spectra are particularly useful in investigating tautomerism and other mobile rearrangements: frequently superposed spectra derived from each form independently are observed. However, if the rearrangement is very fast a 'time-average' spectrum is seen: on heating a sample, the transition between independent and time-averaged spectra is sometimes accessible, permitting calculation of valuable kinetic data. For example, the rearrangement (8 ⇌ 10) *via* (9) has been studied in this way.

8   9   10

8. Mass Spectra

The importance of mass spectra in heterocyclic chemistry has also increased very much recently. The mass spectrum may be obtained from a very small quantity of material; it affords a highly character- istic finger print, and the manner in which the spectral pattern is related to the original structure is becoming apparent to an increas- ing extent. The occurrence of various functional groups may be recognized by their characteristic peaks. High-resolution mass spectroscopy allows determination of the molecular formula of the parent compound, and of any desired fragmentation peak.

Index